TRANSITION AND TRANSFORMATION:
SUCCESSFULLY MANAGING STRESS

TRANSITION AND TRANSFORMATION

SUCCESSFULLY
MANAGING
STRESS

LYNN BRALLIER, RN, MSN, CS

Director, Stress Management Center
Washington, D.C.

FOREWORD BY HANS SELYE, MD

NNR
Los Altos, CA

Project Director: Karen Hoxeng, RN
Illustrations: Deborah Jaffe Miller
Composition: Libra Cold Type
Printing and Binding: Kingsport Press

Library of Congress Cataloging in Publication Data

Brallier, Lynn.
    Transition and transformation: Successfully
    managing stress.

    Bibliography: p.
    Includes index.
    1. Stress (Psychology)   I. Title. [DNLM:
1. Stress, Psychological—Prevention and control.
WM 172 B814t]
BF575.S75B7   1982   158'.1   82-14471
ISBN 0-917010-10-8

The following are acknowledged for granting permission for illustration copy: American Physiological Society; California Raisin Advisory Board; E. P. Dutton, Inc.; Harper & Row, Publishers; Macmillan Publishing Co.; Shelter Publications; Springer-Verlag New York, Inc.; Unity Press; W. B. Saunders Publishing Company; William Morrow & Company, Inc.

A complete credit listing follows the Table of Contents.

Published by National Nursing Review, 342 State Street, Los Altos, CA 94022.

by HANS SELYE

Foreword

Stress management has much to offer in regard to health. The basic determinant of health is homeostasis, which is an issue of the total organism, physical and mental. The aspects of life requiring adaptation, i.e., calling forth the general adaptation syndrome, can be grasped only in terms of one's "life situation."

Stress management aims at enhancing our total well-being, in part through self-awareness and by learning to gauge our own innate energy, potential weaknesses, and strengths. Knowledge of and understanding stress is the way to prevent distress, suffering, and ill health. Stress plays a vital role in helping us cope with everyday problems in our complex and changing society.

Stress is the response of the body to any demand

made upon it. The amount of stress depends on the intensity of the demand, and the ability to cope with the demand will determine its good or bad outcome. As long as we live, there are demands to breathe, to digest our meals, and for the heart to pump blood that circulates throughout the system. Stress is the spice of life when it motivates us to achieve more; this is "eustress," which is good for us. Stress can also defeat us and cause "distress" when we are overcome by it. If distress lasts long enough, it will lead to tissue breakdown in the body or to mental disturbance. Eventually, it will cause such stress-related diseases as high blood pressure, cardiovascular diseases, ulcers, asthma, allergies, and many other psychosomatic illnesses.

Each person must live without creating unnecessary conflicts with his fellow men to ensure peace of mind, to earn goodwill, respect, and even the love of others, as well as to provide himself with a degree of security. Modern society is changing rapidly; such changes deplete adaptation energy. The system does not have time to adjust to one change before another change requires further adaptation. We need an understanding of stress, therefore, to make us aware that our performance and happiness are not optimum. Wellness in body, mind, and spirit will make us more productive, and at the same time our relationships with others will be more harmonious.

Successful stress management finds ways of increasing resistance to stress and reducing its harmful effects. It is also a valuable type of preventive medicine. The inability to cope with stress is the most important issue facing us; hence, managing stress is the answer to most of our health problems and the road to happiness. Indulgence in short-term stress reducers such as smoking, drinking coffee, tea, or alcohol, taking drugs, etc. seems to help us initially, but we soon need ever increasing amounts to get the same effect. Also, these alternatives are all addictive and become problems in themselves. A better method of stress reduction would be relaxation, which involves changes in our attitudes, behaviors, and lifestyles.

Stress management entails a balanced diet in quantities that will ensure optimum weight and good nutrition, routine daily exercise, sufficient sleep to let the body rest and heal itself, and relaxation techniques as described in this book. Stress is the price that mankind has to pay to survive and to accomplish what we consider great things. There should be a proportion between what we want to do and what we can do, between the significance of challenges we rise to meet and the price we have to pay as a consequence; therefore, our goals and priorities should be established accordingly. My best advice to anyone needing help with the stress of life is:

> *Fight for your highest attainable aim,*
> *But do not put up resistance in vain.*

In life it is not what happens to you that matters, but how you take it; therefore, our interpretation of a stressor determines our reaction to it. Lynn Brallier presents very clearly the stress concept and its effect on our health and well-being. She describes in detail the steps needed to control and manage high levels of stress so that it can be made to work for us, and to motivate us to peaks of performance without distress. Her techniques have evolved from her wide experience as a therapist who is conversant with the day-to-day management of clients from all walks of life.

This book is timely and helpful to all of us living and facing the complexities of this industrialized modern society; it teaches us to understand our problems and it gives us the tools needed to solve them so that we can improve the quality of our life.

Hans Selye, CC, MD, PhD, DSC
President
International Institute of Stress

Preface

STRESS — We thrive on it and we die from it. It may push us toward our peak moments or it may disable us for life. Giving an electrifying and brilliant stage performance and delivering a speech of acknowledgement that the opponent has won the election can have similar stressful effects on a human body. Why, then, does one set of stressors seem to invigorate us while another set of stressful situations will point us toward suffering from a wide range of problems, such as hypertension, heart attacks, alcoholism, headaches, arthritis, stomach problems, back pain, accident-proneness, and even cancer? Why is one person's exciting challenge another person's trip to the hospital? These are difficult and important questions. The answers are to be found in training ourselves to be highly aware of our responses to stress and highly competent at preventing and managing stress reactions.

The type, number, intensity, and duration of stress-inducing events are important factors in determining the quality and length of our lives. Even more relevant is how we cope with stress. *Successfully Managing Stress* is designed to assist you in learning to transform distress into manageable stress or even into pleasure so that you can avoid stress illnesses and gain more enjoyment from life. Many books deal with some aspect of stress management. Most are theoretical or focus exclusively on one aspect of controlling stress. *Successfully Managing Stress* presents a holistic approach to stress management in a combination theoretical and experiential format that will allow you to integrate the multiple aspects of assessing and managing stress. Attention is given to the psychophysiology of stress so that your awareness of this bodily process is enhanced. Many ways of evaluating stress, which arises from our environment, our bodies, our minds, and our life philosophies, are presented. Effective and practical stress management methods related to each of these areas are also described in detail.

Successfully Managing Stress is written for health professionals and others who are interested in learning to prevent and handle distress more competently. This book has evolved from my years of experience as a psychotherapist and biofeedback therapist. As Director of the Stress Management Center of Metropolitan Washington, I have taught the material in this book to thousands of people in lectures and workshops. Evaluative comments from a good portion of these people, as well as from clients in my private practice, have been very helpful in designing this as a practical, holistic approach to the problem of assessing and managing stress successfully.

I wish to thank my clients for fully sharing their distress, which has provided the challenges to me to search for solutions. My deepest appreciation goes to Ms. Joan Delaney for her untiring support and skills at typing and editing this manuscript, as well as making creative contributions to its substance.

Lynn Wilson Brallier, RN, MSN, CS
Director
Stress Management Center.

Table of Contents

CHAPTER 1

A HOLISTIC APPROACH TO
STRESS MANAGEMENT

Distress-free Learning 3

Stress-What Is It? 3

Stressors 5

Holistic Conceptualization of Stressors and
  Their Effects 9

Professional Burnout as a Stress Response. 16

  Signs of Burnout: environment, body, mind, spirit. 16

Holism and Stress Management —
  A Clinical Illustration 21

Using this book 26

CHAPTER 2

PSYCHOPHYSIOLOGY OF STRESS

Mind/Body Relationship 29
Psychophysiology Review 33
The Stress Response 40
Stress-Related Illnesses and Disorders 58
   Passive Relaxation to Manage Bodily Distress *126*
      Biofeedback *130*
      Progressive Relaxation *132*
      Autogenics *134*
      Relaxation Tapes *136*
      Imagery *136*
      Meditation *138*
      Body Movement for Relaxation *141*
      Hands-on Methods of Relaxation *142*
      Integrating It All *146*
Management of Special Bodily Distress Problems . . .149
   Obesity *149*
   Pain *150*
   Cancer *152*

CHAPTER 3

STRESS AND THE ENVIRONMENT

Assessing Your Physical Environment 67
   Environmental Questions: climate, pollution, safety *67*
   Personal Questions: food, clothing, colors, nature *69*
Assessing Your Social Environment 72
   Holmes and Rahe Social Readjustment Rating Scale *74*
   Social Systems Theory *76*

Managing Your Physical Environment. 86

    Personal Suggestions: climate, clothing, space, colors *88*

Managing Your Social Environment 90

    Personal Suggestions: self-help groups,

      intimate relationships. *94*

    Awareness of Own Social System *96*

CHAPTER 4

STRESS AND THE BODY

Assessing Your Body for Signs of Distress. 106

    General Body Awareness. *106*

    Physical Reaction to Distress. *106*

    Body Distress Inventory *107*

    Biorhythms and Distress. *112*

    Body Stress Record *116*

Managing Bodily Distress. 116

    Nutrition and Bodily Distress. *117*

    Active Relaxation to Manage Bodily Distress *122*

CHAPTER 5

STRESS AND THE MIND

Mental and Emotional Manifestations of Stress. 160

Self-Assessment of Mental/Emotional Stress 165

    Cognitive Style of Coping *165*

    Assessing Coping with Negative Thoughts and

      Feelings About Self and Others *165*

    Assessing My Patterns of Dealing with Control Issues *169*

Assessing My Patterns of Coping with
  Strong Emotions *170*
Assessing My Goal Setting Style *172*
Assessing Patterns of Coping with Frustration. *173*
Personality Style of Coping with Stress *174*
Life Style and Managing Stress. *179*

Managing Stressors by Managing the Mind. 183
Avoidance of Stressors *184*
Accommodation to Stressors *185*
Regulation of Mental/Emotional Reactions
  to Stressors *186*
Self-Regulation of Beliefs *189*

Self-Regulation of Emotional Responses 201
Fear *202*
Anger *207*
Guilt. *213*
Anxiety. *216*
Depression *222*
Perfectionism *230*
Insomnia *232*
Loneliness *235*
Addictive Behavior *237*
Sexual Dysfunctions *239*

Using Knowledge and Experience to
  Regulate Stressors 241
Decision Making *241*
Goal Setting. *242*
Time Management. *243*

CHAPTER 6

STRESS AND THE SPIRIT

Assessing Your Spiritual Beliefs. 255

Questionnaire: Assessment of Spiritual Beliefs/Values . . . *257*

Questionnaire: Effects of Spiritual Beliefs on
Managing Stress. *262*

Managing Stress from a Spiritual Perspective. 268

Communicating with a Greater Power: prayer,
meditation, imagery. *269*

Healing as a Spiritual Experience *276*

Hazards and Rewards of Spiritual Growth *277*

ILLUSTRATION RESOURCE CREDITS

CHAPTER 1

A Holistic Approach to Stress Management

Life can be viewed as a constant flow of changes. These changes are internal and external, complex and simple, profound and superficial, lasting and momentary, pleasureful and painful. Each change, no matter what its characteristics, requires us to react in an adaptive manner to protect our psychophysiological integrity. Whether we must suddenly make alternative vacation plans or react to the death of someone close, we enter a period of complex imbalance which must be restored. Most often the stress responses we experience as we adapt to changes are well within normal limits. We simply deal with whatever challenge we perceive, and our homeostatic, fairly relaxed state returns.

Most of our stress responses are not harmful to us; however, managing stress well is no longer an optional talent, but a health-protecting and life-saving tool because we live in times when the rate of change we experience is increasing dramatically. A high rate or high intensity of unpleasant events can trigger stress responses that can cause major health problems and death. Both the length and quality of our lives depend to a significant degree on the ability to become experts at coping with stressful life events.

Competence in managing stress leaves us free to be aware of and live out our finest inner potential as human beings such as developing our creativity and enjoyment of life. Learning to channel the energy which is available from a stress arousal state into a creative endeavor is highly rewarding as well as health-saving. A well-developed ability to manage stress and be at ease is apparently important even in our love life. Walster recently reported a study that rated characteristics most appealing to the opposite sex. The study indicated that typical characteristics such as physical appearance, personality, wealth, and social position are secondary to a relaxed appearance.[1]

We all experience stress and cope with it by using learned patterns of thoughts, feelings, and behaviors. By reading this book and practicing the suggested exercises, you can expand your repertoire and make more choices for managing stress in your life. More knowledge of and control over your own ways of responding to stress can be of great personal value. Professionally, too, you will find that new knowledge and personal experience with stress reduction helps in teaching your clients to prevent health problems and effectively handle the problems they are currently experiencing.

Because professionals in the health care field are exposed to a high rate and intensity of change, they run a risk of depleting their own adaptation energy when faced with such stressors as too many demands on their nurturing skills or too much conflict in work situations. When these kinds of specific risks are added to "normal" life changes and demands, the health professional is confronted with more than the usual pressure to cope well with stress or pay the penalties.

Distress-free Learning?

Any change, including changes you will make as you learn the material in this text, can be stressful. You may want to offset this stress by trying some or all of the following suggestions. First, see if you can visualize yourself as a true expert in stress management. See yourself moving gracefully from one change to the next, staying healthy and challenged about living or coming back to this state easily even after a crisis. Let yourself trust that learning from this book will help you add to your present knowledge and move toward this goal of graceful coping.

Second, read this material only when you actually feel you want to do so. Encourage yourself but do not force yourself to do every suggested exercise. This type of approach will help avoid the pain of forced learning.

Third, practice what you learn as soon as possible so that you get feedback quickly about your ability to control your own stress level. You may even want to reward yourself in some way at the end of each section or chapter or just after you feel sure that you have assimilated some new way of dealing with stress.

Stress – What Is It?

In a very general way stress can be defined as a state of arousal or mobilization of an organism. It is a degree of agitation that can be experienced internally and at times can be noted by an external observer of the organism.

In psychological terms, stress can be described as the experience we have when the demands we place upon ourselves or are placed upon us exceed our perceived ability to cope with them. Everyone is familiar with this emotional state and the bodily tension and upset that accompany this state of mind.

Although some disagreement exists in the scientific community about the basic psychophysiologic principles involved in stress reactions, consideration of the work of Cannon[2] and Selye[3] is vital in defining stress. Walter Cannon, a Harvard physiologist, coined the term *homeostasis*, meaning the ability of our bodies to stay in a stable state of balance. In the early 1900s, Cannon focused his research on threats to homeostasis, or balance, and how our bodies deal with these threats so that stability is maintained. He outlined many highly specialized adjustment mechanisms that protect the body from imbalances in blood sugar, hydration, temperature, and the ability to defend against microbes. Cannon noticed that certain emotional reactions such as fear and rage were also a threat to homeostasis. His now familiar fight or flight syndrome, describing the body's reaction to stressful events, is a major consideration in the psychophysiology of stress.

Another well-known figure in the field of stress is Hans Selye, a Canadian endocrinologist, now President of the International Institute of Stress in Montreal. Selye is best known for research in the area of specific and general adjustment reactions in the body during stressful events. He defines the general adaptation syndrome as a nonspecific reaction to stress that is also an attempt to adapt and maintain homeostasis. Stress, then, is a nonspecific response of the body to any demand and is as essential to life as the air we breathe. Selye acknowledges the destructive effects on the body when stress is not controlled. According to Selye, there are two basic kinds of stress. One is discomfort, or *distress*, in which the body goes through the nonspecific response and heads toward exhaustion, disease, or even death. The second variety of stress, usually exciting and even happy, is *eustress*. Again, the body undergoes virtually the same nonspecific response, but less damage is done and more pleasure and a sense of growth are evident. Comparison of these two views of the body's attempt to maintain homeostasis will be presented in more detail in a later chapter.

Some confusion about the use of the word *stress* exists in literature on the subject and in our general language. Selye uses stress to indicate the body's reactions to a force, whereas physicists define stress as the force itself. A physicist or engineer will talk about stress that causes strain or a physical change in the material acted upon. Selye, however, uses the term *stressors* to indicate the forces that cause a reaction or "stress" in the body.

In this book the word *stressor* indicates the force that produces strain, stress, the stress response, distress, and eustress. The term *stress response* includes the psychophysiology described by both Cannon and Selye.

Stressors

If you think about the incredibly wide range of stressors—the forces of change that tamper with homeostasis—you may find it remarkable that you are still alive and alert enough to read these words. In reality, almost any object, situation, or perception can act as a stressor and disturb our balance to some degree. Any one of such diverse events as a virus, a car accident, a wedding, a promotion at work, feelings of lowered self-esteem, or the loss of a direction for one's life can precipitate an intense stress syndrome in our bodies. Although there seem to be some universally threatening stressors like nearly being killed, it is also clear that what is highly stressful to one person may go virtually unnoticed by another. We can see, then, that a stressor may be frightening, challenging, anger provoking, motivating, fun, or obnoxious. Our responses to stressors range from easy recovery of our homeostasis and feelings of well-being to no full recovery when we may become chronically ill or die quickly. Sometimes people confuse the *quality of the stressor* and the *quality of the response* to stressors. For instance, you may say that your work is challenging and interesting and assume that you are not reacting to it with any kind of stress response. Not true. Even continual eustress, although apparently easier to recover from, can be harmful. So while the quality of the stressor may be positive in terms of being highly motivating, challenging, or even fun, the quality of our response to that stressor may vary from a mild rise in blood pressure to a sudden fatal heart attack.

While all stressors represent change of some sort, many of them also involve the loss of something valued. There are unlimited sources of stressors, and to complicate matters, they vary in intensity, duration, probability, clarity, and controllability. Let's get a closer look at each of the characteristics of stressors.

First is intensity. Look at Figure 1, a drawing of the stressor intensity continuum. This simple illustration shows the range of reactions to the intensity of stimulation. Remember that reactions will vary a great deal among individuals since intensity is usually a matter of personalized perception and evaluation. The point remains, however, that intensity of a stressor can have a

STRESSOR INTENSITY CONTINUUM

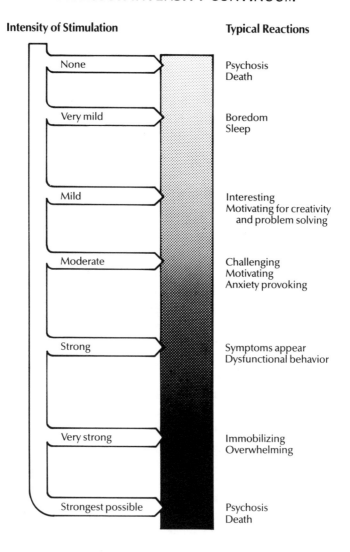

Figure 1: Stressor intensity continuum illustrates the range of reactions to the intensity of stimulation.

wide range of effects, some in our best interest and some not.

Second, duration of contact with a stressor is an important variable. Just as a one-second exposure of the skin to a caustic chemical is less stressful than a five-minute exposure, so is a two-day period of being low on money much less distressing than being equally short of money for two months. Usually people succumb to the cumulative effects of a stressor over time. There are exceptions to this, however. If the stressor is a common part of life, people may eventually utilize defense mechanisms or some healthy method of managing distress to adapt to the stressor. An example of this would be "tuning out" the noise of aircraft if one's home is located under a flight pattern for landing.

The third variable is the probability of a stressor occurring. Our personality traits affect this variable as do our physical and social context and our developmental stages, among others. In terms of development, for example, the probabilities are fairly well-defined regarding the time in our lives we will go through the stress of events such as starting school, raising children, and coping with the psychophysiological changes of aging. This probability factor at least provides some predictability to help us curtail the effects of these stressors.

Fourth is a characteristic of stressors I call the clarity, or awareness, factor. Have you ever experienced a sense of distress, a feeling that "something" was wrong, when you could not concretely identify that "something" and deal with it? While some stressors are painfully obvious and can at least be faced, others defy our ability to be sure and clear about our perceptions. If another person sends you hostile messages through subtle body language, for example, you may not know immediately why you are uncomfortable. When we are unable or unwilling to be fully aware of a stressor but are aware of discomfort, the lack of clarity itself becomes a stressor.

The last factor is the element of "controllability" of the stressor. Whether a stressor is viewed as controllable or not will vary from one person to the next and will vary with personal experience and other contextual factors. Much has been written on the need in laboratory animals and people for a sense of internal control over events in life—especially those events with harmful, painful, or frustrating consequences.[4] Generally speaking, it seems that having a strong sense of internal control is important in preventing stressful experiences, while having a moderate sense of control is more helpful in managing a stressful event. These findings will be discussed in more detail in Chapter Four. A concept related to internal-external Locus of Control is that of a "sense of coherence," the confidence that things are likely to work out as well as possible. Antonovsky[5] declares this confidence to be vital in managing stressors well. This sense of coherence will be expanded in Chapter Four.

Holistic Conceptualization of Stressors and Their Effects

The management of stressors and their effects has become an incredibly complex process. Attempts to avoid complexity have led to numerous articles and books on managing stress that read as if they were written by one of the proverbial blind men who, after inspecting one portion of the elephant, then describes the entire beast. By looking at stress and its management through a holistic framework, we will hopefully "see" the wholeness of the elephant. Support for this conceptual framework comes from Selye, who says:

"A real understanding of stress is therefore essentially dependent upon a holistic and integrative approach; no special aspect of it can be analyzed in depth without a full realization of where and how it fits into the whole picture."[6]

This book is organized from the vantage point of holistic health theory and takes into account the individual's environment, body, mind, and spirit when assessing needs and developing a program of health assistance. As most of you are aware, holism has become a conceptual framework for health care delivery in this country in the past few years. A holistic health model, in fact, has emerged as a viable companion to the predominant and familiar medical model.

Historically, holistic health care began with shamans, who were the healers in ancient cultures. The shamans viewed healing as the restoration of balance among the physical, spiritual, and social aspects of the sick one. The Greeks also realized that the body could be diseased because of disharmony of the mind and that healing in a lasting sense involved the spiritual healing of the person. In fact, the word *holistic* comes from the Greek word *holos*, meaning whole, in recognition that we are more than the sum of our parts.

In more recent times, holism has been espoused by Gestalt therapists, family therapists, and country doctors. The word *Gestalt* literally means whole. The concern of Gestalt therapists is that the client be able to experience as much wholeness or potential as a human being as possible. When one's wholeness can be experienced in a balanced and integrated way, one is in a high level state of wellness. Family therapists also utilize the systems theory, which concerns the relationship of part and whole (family member and entire extended family).

Some of you, especially those who grew up in the country, remember the family doctor, who was part of the community and was perhaps the only doctor available. Most of these doctors practiced a form of holistic medicine by nature of their involvement in the community, since they had information on their clients' environment, mental and emotional state, and spiritual philosophy, along with the physical findings obtained from office or home visits. Since then, of course, medicine has gone through a technological revolution, and physicians in general have become a bit more mechanistic in their approach to clients. The physician may pay more attention to the disease process than to the person who has the "dis-ease." In the past two decades physicians have also tended toward reductionistic thinking about health problems and have paid only a minor degree of attention to the psychological aspects of illness and a minute degree of attention to any effects the client's spiritual or philosophical beliefs might have on his or her health.

The trend has reversed, however, in the past few years. Humanism and holism have become increasingly apparent in some areas of traditional medical practice. Emphasis on family practice as a specialty for physicians and holistically-oriented nurse practitioner roles are evidence of this trend. Holistic theory has also influenced the practice of psychophysiologic medicine. Psychosomatic medicine specialists have usually focused on explaining how clients' worries and emotional states influence their physical disease processes. Now some practitioners are wondering about the reverse, that is, how to help clients use their mental and emotional states to prevent stress and heal their bodies.

Throughout this book holistic health principles and goals will be applied to stress management. One holistic health goal, for instance, is high level wellness. This is more than the absence of disease. If you have attained a high level of wellness, you are free of physical signs and symptoms of illness, are notably enthusiastic and creative, have mutually rewarding relationships with others, and have a clear sense of purpose and meaning in life. Obviously, you must be an expert in managing stress to attain these goals. The following chapters have been written with high level wellness in mind, and I would encourage you to adopt this level of wellness as a goal for yourself right now so that you will be likely to put what you read into practice in your own life.

Another principle of holistic health that applies easily to stress management is self-responsibility. This is the acknowledgment that no one else can manage your stress except you. You must heal yourself, especially if you are a health professional engaged in the healing of others. Take some time right now to think about this idea of self-responsibility for stress management. Have you been expecting others to lessen your stress or to encourage you to take it easier? Have you been blaming others for making your life stressful? Determine now what sense of commitment you have to taking full responsibility for your own stress management. Allow yourself to experience a sense of partnership with this book as helper to you if you are willing to claim responsibility for controlling your level of stress and improving your health generally.

The personal mediating factors of environment, body, mind, and spirit that help us manage stressors effectively serve as later chapter headings. By using the word mind, I include both the mental and emotional aspects of our being. By spirit I refer to that part of us which may also be called our "higher self" and can experience oneness with the positive forces of the universe or God. It is the part of us that allows us to experience transcendence of sensory reality and be inspired. Even though these areas are discussed separately, holism prevails and you will see that these areas become integrated and balanced as you practice stress management methods. Also integrated are combinations of Eastern and Western traditions in health care. Concepts such as homeostasis, balance, and harmony are very important to effective stress management. Being able to balance such things as pleasure and responsibility, work and family, and attention to self and others are crucial to successfully controlling your stress level.

Conceptual Model

A conceptual model of the ideas presented thus far is shown in Figure 2. At a glance you can see why stress management issues are often quite complex. Thus advice to "take it easy" or "avoid it" are inadequate solutions for coping with stressors. This is especially clear when you realize that the diagram symbolizes a pulsating, dynamic, ever-changing life and its context.

Upon closer inspection, two things become particularly noteworthy. First is the notion that the environment, body, mind, and spirit of the person are involved in each step of the process of dealing with a stressor. Although a stressor may originate from one discrete source, such as a hurricane (physical), or loss of an important friendship (social), heart attack (body), loss of self-esteem (mind), or loss of sense of purpose (spiritual), the results are not as clear in other categories. For instance we may use personal mediating factors in the form of both bodily and spiritual sources or any other combination to begin to cope with stressors. The same is true for the categories called "stress response" and

STRESSORS: CONCEPTUAL MODEL

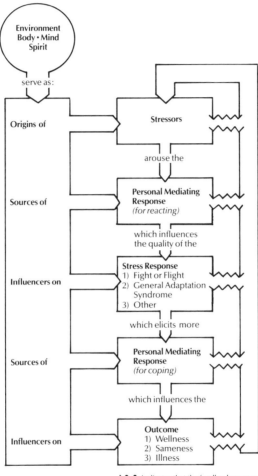

Figure 2A: Conceptual model of stressors and their effects as viewed holistically.

PERSONAL MEDIATING FACTORS

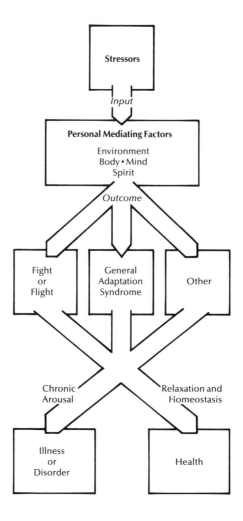

Figure 2B: Personal mediating factors can be used in various combinations to help us manage stress.

"outcome." *Warning:* Trying to keep track of all the permutations in yourself or in your clients could be hazardous to your stress level!

A second important observation is that at each of the four steps in the process something can function inadequately and produce stressor(s). It is possible, of course, that the "personal mediating factors" can thoroughly cope with a stressor and no trace of a "stress response" result is found, but this is not likely unless the stressor was exceedingly weak in its impact.

Professional Burnout As a Stress Response

Now that we have defined a conceptual model for understanding stress and managing it, let's see how it applies to one of the hazards we face—professional burnout. Storlie[7] has defined burnout in nursing as the disillusionment nurses feel when reality does not match their ideals and hope for change is nearly nonexistent. Burnout is the resignation to the feeling of the lack of power to make a difference. Burnout affects people at every level of being. It affects our social milieu, our bodily functioning, our mental and emotional state, and our spiritual life.

You probably know someone who complains of being burned out professionally or perhaps you have even experienced this syndrome yourself. Some of the typical signs of professional burnout are listed below. These signs of burnout can be evident both when a person is actually on the job or is at home.

Environment   One sign of burnout, as manifested in a person's physical environment, is an uncharacteristic lack of attention to the organization and cleanliness of the environment. How one relates to the social environment may also indicate signs of burnout. On a hospital unit, for example, the domino theory may occur—if one nurse begins to suffer burnout and becomes argumentative or silently hostile or begins to miss days of work, other staff members are negatively affected. The person suffering burnout may initiate hostile and defensive interactions with others and may be of little or no support to the team members. If group cohesion breaks down, small factions of the staff may begin warring with one another. These skirmishes may lead to people becoming withdrawn and isolated from one another. Occasionally, people may try to compensate for this malfunctioning social system by seeming to work harder and even putting in overtime hours, but the efficiency ratio is probably lowered due to the emotional energy drain they are experiencing. Eventually, of course, this burnout syndrome spreads and causes hostile interactions among shifts, heightening the typical tensions that usually exist among people from different shifts.

Body Chronic fatigue and exhaustion are common complaints when a person is in burnout. Feeling the need to sleep for long hours, but not awaking refreshed, is also common. Even taking days off does not seem to restore one's energy for very long. Sexual energy can also dissipate. Minor pain and physical ailments, such as headaches, gastrointestinal problems, aches from muscle tension, and frequent infections, are classical signs of burnout. Any psychophysiological response, however, is possible as a sign of burnout.

Mind Mental signs of burnout are confusion, disorientation, and even very mild episodes of brief dissociative reactions. Also common is an increase over the normal number of negative thoughts about oneself and others.

Emotionally, a person feels overwhelmed, helpless, depressed, hostile, guilty, and pervasively negative. Not only may feelings of compassion and caring be diminished, but they are sometimes replaced by feelings of "who cares?" Often during burnout a person's mental and emotional functioning and body tension may be so great as to cause some form of sleep disturbance. One may feel incredibly bored and exhausted but be unable to obtain restful sleep.

Spirit The disillusionment factor in burnout can be very disruptive spiritually, leading to many questions about nursing and life in general. A nurse in burnout may find herself wondering what happened to her intention to compassionately care for sick people and help them toward wellness. She may also find herself rather cynically facing the question, "What is life all about anyway?"

Let's take a look now at some of the major stressors that precipitate the burnout experience in work. Unfortunately, in any work situation, thousands of external potential stressors are present that may contribute to professional burnout. External pressures in a nurse's working environment usually involve both administrative and clinical sources. Some common causes of burnout are lack of administrative support, lack of sufficient staff (with consequent time pressure leading to errors and inefficiency), shift work (with subsequent irregularity in sleep and eating patterns), assignment to unfamiliar units, lack of peace and quiet in the work area, and feelings of being powerless to control the volume of work in terms of client flow. The consequent rapid turnover of staff working on any particular shift or unit adds even more distress for the remaining staff people, who must put forth energy to greet and integrate a new staff person while grieving the loss of a familiar person. Head nurses are particularly vulnerable to burnout since they suffer managerial stressors as well as clinical ones.

The clinical nurse is also faced with many burnout triggers even if she manages to spend a high percentage of her time in clinical rather than administrative tasks. Technological changes can be fairly constant and demanding. Becoming involved and committed to caring for someone, especially for the critically ill or dying, can be an extreme drain on energy. The nurse may also find the client's family to be highly anxious and in need of additional attention and time. In an intensive care situation, there may be difficult ethical issues involving life and death. These issues, plus the nurse's feelings of loss and perhaps failure when a client dies, can add up to a formidable sense of exhaustion and depletion if these decisions and feelings are a typical part of the work week.

Conflicts among the staff and among various disciplines working together on a unit are another vast source of stressors. Personality conflicts can abound and role ambiguity can run rampant. One may feel a sense of dissatisfaction with one's role, perhaps because educational ideals for roles and "real world" roles do not match. Brief[8] and others report that nurses who have earned their bachelor's degrees report more role stress than other nurses, apparently because they feel underutilized. Another frequent complaint relative to burnout is nurses' difficulties relating to physicians. Nurses complain that physicians do not listen to them or respect their judgment, and this devaluing leads to many negative, energy-depleting feelings.

Some common internal sources of distress are also related to burnout. Heading the list, says Scully[9], is expecting too much of oneself. Scully believes that teaching nurses total client care and a holistic approach has led somehow to the idea that the nurses must be "all things to all people." She claims that "expecting too much of oneself can lead to burnout faster than any other single stressor." Also important as a source of internal distress is one's actual or perceived lack of knowledge, which leads to poor clinical performance at times and lowered self-esteem.

Management of burnout involves changes in the individual as well as the organization. At an organizational level nurses must have adequate orientation programs to become thoroughly accustomed to the philosophy, policies, procedures, and technology of that particular work place. At best, policies will be clear and fair and will include nurses from all levels in their formulation. Administrative policies that allow for pay equal to other professionals at similar levels and liberal support of opportunities for inservice and continuing education, quiet time during a shift, and "mental health" days off are invaluable in preventing burnout. Adequate administrative support and peer support groups are also very important, as is adequate staffing with a minimum of floating and shift changes.

To manage or prevent burnout on a personal level, many strategies are necessary. Being aware of signs of burnout within oneself is of primary importance. If not aware of these signs, a person may believe that trying harder is the answer. When the already overextended person tries harder, more energy depletion occurs. In desperation, the person may begin to use drugs or alcohol or a combination of the two. Drugs and alcohol represent only one dysfunctional way of handling signs of burnout. Fortunately, there are many interesting and even exciting ways to handle burnout and distress in a more general sense. This is what the following chapters are about. One aspect of personal management of burnout and distress is so basic and important that it must be mentioned now. Inner strength, both spiritual and emotional in nature, is the strength that is needed to maintain one's integrity, ideals, and awareness of the finest parts of our own nature in spite of external reality. As Storlie[10] says, "Whether the strength comes through family ties, through religion and love of God, through fondness for animals, or in other ways, is unimportant. What is important is that the nurse believe in herself and cling to the most cherished of her ideals with a tenacity that cannot easily be undone." This kind of internal strength allows us to transcend many everyday stressors.

Holism and Stress Management—A Clinical Illustration

In my work as a family and Gestalt psychotherapist and biofeedback therapist, I help people learn to manage stress utilizing both educational and clinical approaches. The educational approach includes lectures, workshops, and a course I teach regularly in stress management and meditation. This course is taught privately as well as being sponsored by universities, hospitals, and businesses. Although the workshops or the course varies according to the needs of group members, I usually incorporate some biofeedback experience, material on assessment of stressors and stress responses, and material on the relaxation response, nutrition, exercise, psychological attitudes, interpersonal systems, stressors, and spiritual philosophy. An important part of the course is each participant's disciplined practice of a relaxation tape. The tape is called "Suggestions for General Relaxation" (Brallier[11]) which I constructed from my clinical experience in making many individualized relaxation and self-regulation tapes for biofeedback clients. It contains suggestions for body and mind relaxation and is rather hypnotic in nature. When the tape is practiced regularly, people find that they increase their expertise at eliciting a relaxation response to counter the stress response. The remaining task then becomes the integration of the relaxation response into daily life.

The clinical approach to managing stress is through my independent practice of holistic health that focuses on stress management, psychotherapy, and biofeedback. Since the scope of my practice is so broad, my clients come for relief of distress from a wide range of stress-related or stress-induced illnesses. Also, since my practice is located on Capitol Hill in Washington, D.C., I am accustomed to dealing with people in public office or their family or staff members who are showing signs of distress and burnout. Other government workers and health professionals also come for help in managing stress. I see people who are chronically depressed as well as those who are in acute depression from a crisis situation. Many of my clients have psychophysiologic problems that are stress-induced, such as heart problems, hypertension, ulcers, colitis, migraine and tension headaches, and back pain. Approximately one-third of my clinical practice deals with people who have cancer and who want to manage the subsequent distress from both the disease and the treatment process. Many of these clients want to change their personalities and lifestyles to help avoid a recurrence if they go into remission at this time. Biofeedback, meditation, and imagery methods have proven very powerful for these clients in the management of side effects of treatments, pain, depression, helplessness, and perhaps in the reactivation of the immune system.

The following clinical situation will illustrate a ho-

listic approach to stress management. The client request-
ed the evaluation session after he was discharged from
the hospital following a myocardial infarction. The client
wanted to learn ways to better manage stress in order to
avoid another serious heart attack. In the initial contact
by telephone, I had given the client the option of taking
a stress management and meditation course or being
seen for a clinical evaluation. He chose the clinical evaluation since he felt he needed immediate individualized
attention.

Robert is 40 years old and works as an administrative assistant for a senator. He had no history of
heart trouble and has no other major health problems. He is overweight, complains of difficulty in
sleeping for several years now, and has occasional
depressive episodes, which he has attempted to
handle by either working harder or becoming in-
toxicated with alcohol. He does admit to overuse of
alcohol on a daily basis and is concerned about his
occasional enjoyment of cocaine at social functions.
Robert complains mainly of burnout signs related to his work. Although he admires and supports
his boss, he also competes with him and secretly
believes he would make a better senator. Added to
this very demanding job is the fact that Robert sells
real estate in his "spare" time. Another area of concern is his marriage. Robert has been married for 21
years and has two daughters, one in college and the
other a senior in high school. He complains that his
marriage is dull except for an explosive argument
every few weeks. Robert has been having affairs
with other women regularly for the past few years,
but does not enjoy a full sense of satisfaction from
this lifestyle.

Questions about Robert's nutrition and exercise are deferred since he is presently in a cardiac rehabilitation program, which daily monitors his diet and exercise. A biofeedback diagnostic indicates that Robert has very high muscle tension and a moderately low hand temperature, both of which can indicate chronic distress. A discussion of Robert's emotional status leads to evaluation of his sense of himself spiritually. He reports that he is not a religious person and that his depressions occasionally take the form of "Is this all there is?" Robert is unable to verbalize a coherent spiritual philosophy but says his heart attack led him to wonder more about his own purposes in life and his connection with what he refers to as "some higher power than myself." As a way to investigate this area of his life, Robert has chosen to read books on the spiritual beliefs of various cultures.

Robert is easy to work with since he is very highly motivated to save his own life. We begin with biofeedback practice each session, and he practices the relaxation tape three times each day at home and at his office. Soon a system is set up to help remind him to relax many times during the day so that he can integrate his newly learned relaxation response into his work and home life. He also utilizes various imagery methods to relax and control muscle tension and the vascular system. Later he is able to use the tape once a day and practices a ten-minute meditation twice a day. Since the beginning of his program, Robert has also seen a massage therapist, who has helped him greatly reduce muscle tension, balance his body energies, improve his posture so that his chest cavity is not constricted, and become more aware of all of these things so that he can regulate them during the day himself.

Robert is an avid reader and has enjoyed studying several books on stress management and relaxation. His enthusiasm and disciplined work show results very quickly and soon he is able to notice that he is less irritable, has more patience with others and himself, and is able to say no at times rather than keeping frenetically busy responding to others' demands and the demands he places upon himself. Robert also shows some evidence of lifestyle changes, such as more time for entertainment, relaxing social occasions, and quiet time alone. He also reports that the meditation has helped him gather internal strength to help prevent his usual depressive episodes and has helped him be more aware of his own spiritual nature.

Individual psychotherapy is focused on Robert's low self-esteem and patterns from childhood which drive him to overachieve in order to prove his worth as a person. Robert and his wife are seen for couples therapy to reassess their values, their goals, and their sexual relationship. Although both these forms of psychotherapy are difficult for Robert, he is able to utilize them for a satisfactory outcome. He is able to terminate his clinical appointments feeling a high level of confidence that he can avoid another heart attack and find more pleasure and meaning in his work and personal life.

As you can see from this brief clinical presentation, many areas of distress were identified. These were noted in much more detail than could be reported here. For guidelines in assessing the stress level of clients in hospitals, refer to Meissner's Hospital Stress Rating Scale.[12] Doing a thorough stress assessment from a holistic framework is not too time-consuming and provides a strong base upon which to build clinical interventions.

Using This Book

After the following chapter on psychophysiology, each of the next four chapters follows a similar format. First you will be guided to assess your environment, body, mind, or spirit. Then you will look at and practice ways to manage these particular stressors. Take time to review sections that seem particularly important to you. Also consider doing the exercises more than once, especially if you have a sense that your responses may change or intensify as you proceed through the book.

If you become more aware of specific problems as you do the assessment section of each chapter, be sure to evaluate possible need for professional assistance in further assessment rather than automatically assuming that a problem is "only" a stress symptom and tossing it off. You may also discover while participating in some of the exercises in this book that the self-help format is too simplistic to get at the depth of some stress reactions. If this happens, consider seeking professional consultation.

In the process of using this book, you may discover that you are addicted to the stress in your life. Part of you may complain about it while another part gets great rewards or secondary gains from staying in distress. In my work with businesses and hospitals, I find many managerial people who unconsciously "need" their stress symptoms to demonstrate to their organization how devoted and hardworking they are. Or a parent may "need" to stay distressed to show the children how hard they are working to provide for them. Some people have developed a pattern of gleaning almost all of their excitement in life from starting "stress fires" and rushing to put them out. Reasons for being addicted to stress are prolific and varied. Being aware of your own reasons and making a conscious decision about retaining stressors and distress reactions, softening them, or letting them go is healthier than continuing blindly in patterns of distress which are determined unconsciously.

If you "enjoy" stress in your life, it is still safe to read this book. It will not push you to stamp out every shred of stress and go into isolation. The book is designed instead to help you successfully sort out those stressors you want in your life and how you want to react to them. Guided learning experiences are provided to help you toward the goal of facing life with full gusto and excitement while avoiding the crippling effects of stress-related accidents and illnesses.

REFERENCES

1. Walster, E., and Walster, G. W. *A New Look at Love.* Reading, MA: Addison-Wesley Publishing Company, 1978.

2. Cannon, W. B. *The Wisdom of the Body.* New York: W. W. Norton & Co., Inc., 1932; *Bodily Changes in Pain, Hunger, Fear, and Rage.* 2nd ed. Boston: Charles T. Branford Co., 1953.

3. Selye, H. *Stress Without Distress.* New York: The New American Library, Inc. 1975; *Stress in Health and Disease.* Reading, MA: Butterworths, 1976; *The Stress of Life.* Rev. ed. New York: McGraw-Hill Book Co., 1978.

4. Perlmutter, L. C., and Monty, R. A. "The Importance of Perceived Control: Fact or Fantasy?" *American Scientist*, 1977, 65, 759-765.

5. Antonovsky, A. *Health, Stress, and Coping.* San Francisco: Jossey-Bass, 1979.

6. Selye, H. *Stress in Health and Disease.* Reading, MA: Butterworths, 1976.

7. Storlie, F. J. "Burnout: The Elaboration of a Concept." *American Journal of Nursing,* December 1979, pp. 2108-2111.

8. Brief, A. P., Van Sell, M., Aldag, R. J., and Malone, N. "Anticipation of Role Stress Among Registered Nurses." *Journal of Health and Social Behavior,* June 1979, *20,* 161-166.

9. Scully, R. "Stress in the Nurse." *American Journal of Nursing,* May 1980, pp. 912-915.

10. Storlie, F. J. "Burnout: The Elaboration of a Concept." *American Journal of Nursing,* December 1979, pp. 2108-2111.

11. Brallier, L. W. "Suggestions for General Relaxation." Cassette tape, 1978. Available from 621 Maryland Avenue, NE, Washington, DC 20002.

12. Meissner, J. E. "Measuring Patient Stress with the Hospital Stress Rating Scale." *Nursing 80,* August, 70-71.

CHAPTER 2

Psychophysiology of Stress

The material in this chapter will highlight mind/body dynamics as they exist in a normal state and during a stress response. We will look at how environmental, spiritual, and psychosocial influences affect the central nervous system, the autonomic nervous system, the endocrine system, and various structural and functional systems of the body. We will also see how the stress response, when too intense or too frequent, takes its toll in the form of illnesses and other disorders.

Mind/Body Relationship

The word *psychophysiology* can be misleading since it connotes an interaction between two separate parts of a human being. This dualism is a seventeenth century influence of the philosopher Rene Descartes, who viewed nature as divided into two separate independent realms of reality—mind and matter. This mechanistic world view was also supported by Newton's theory of physics and has strongly influenced the development of attitudes about the relationship of mind and body in the health care professions. Early psychosomatic medicine demonstrated a clear connection between mind and body, and contemporary psychophysiology acknowledges highly complex feedback loops that help explain interactions between feeling states and bodily conditions.

Currently, the study of the mind/body response to stress is made more complicated by the influence of modern quantum physics and mysticism. Fundamental to both physicists and mystics is the idea that there exists a cosmic wholeness, that the universe is an indivisible reality, and that there are no separate objects and events. This basic oneness idea, when applied to the definition of a human being, allows us to see that we are an indivisible totality and that there exists an inseparable mind/body unity. Elmer and Alyce Green,[1] two of this country's pioneers in biofeedback research, hypothesize that the mind is an energy structure and that the body is simply the densest part of the mind. Representatives of the new physics, such as Fritjof Capra,[2] explain mind/body unity by describing atomic reality according to quantum physics theory. This theory describes subatomic particles in terms of probabilities rather than discrete, solid pieces of matter. Subatomic particles, rather than existing in definite places, show instability and can only be defined in terms of "tendencies to exist" and "tendencies to occur." These particles form dynamic patterns or "energy bundles," says Capra, and, in turn, form stable molecular structures, which give a solid aspect to some material substances like our bodies. Our

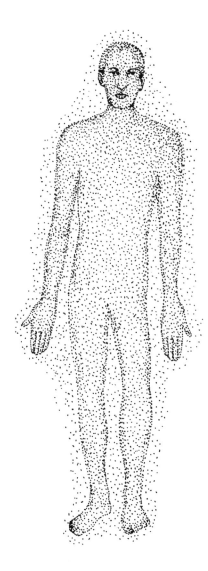

Figure 3: Illustration of a person as an "energy form."

minds, then, are the same subatomic particles and dynamic patterns but exhibit less density (see Figure 3). This way of viewing reality agrees with statements by many mystics. LeShan[3] demonstrates this by mixing "nature of reality" statements made by mystics and by physicists and challenging his readers to sort the list. The reader finds that although the style of language varies, the essence of the statements agree. Recently Carl Pribram[4] and David Bohm[5] have presented theories of the universe as a holograph (every aspect of the universe is whole and has every quality of the universe itself within it). This idea is particularly relevant to studies of brain functioning and will probably have future implications for understanding psychophysiology and the stress response.

The new physics, mysticism, and holographic theory are important concepts to keep in mind when viewing your experiences from a holistic standpoint. We will discuss the mind's influence on bodily reactions or conditions and the manifestation of the mind itself through the body, but will not lose sight of the ultimate knowledge that mind and body are one.

Take a moment now to experience the oneness of your own mind/body by experimenting with imagery. As you read, let your mind form clear, visual images. Begin by imagining that you are walking in a desert. The day is hot and windy. The wind is dry, the sun is hot, and the sand is very hot on your feet. You can feel your lips and mouth getting very dry. In fact, your lips, mouth, and throat all feel parched from the dry, hot air blowing relentlessly over your body. Now clearly visualize your own kitchen and imagine that you have just come in from that desert and want to relieve the extreme dryness in your mouth and throat. Imagine that you are stepping toward your refrigerator and that when you open it you see a beautiful, plump yellow lemon. You reach into the refrigerator and pick it up, feel its texture and its coldness, and place it on a cutting board. You find a very sharp knife and slice the lemon in half, watching the juice run down onto the cutting board. You take the knife and slice a section from one of the halves and again the juice flows gently from the lemon onto the cutting board. At this point you can wait no longer and pick up a piece of the lemon, put it directly into your mouth, bite down on it, and taste the juice as you bite.

If you have been imaging this scene in detail and with clarity, you will notice that you are salivating at this point simply from creating a visual image. A specific image has elicited a specific physiological response. This experience illustrates the rather instantaneous physiological response to a mental image and helps us understand how easy it is for our mental and emotional states to influence our bodily states. Keep this experience in mind (so to speak) as you learn more about the specific psychophysiology of stress.

Psychophysiology Review

Before we focus on the details of the stress response, let's briefly review psychophysiology, with an emphasis on neuroendocrinology since the nervous system and endocrine system and the wealth of feedback loops within and between these two systems are most relevant to the psychophysiology of the stress response. First we will review the structure and function of the central nervous system and then outline some of the relationships that exist between the central nervous system, the autonomic nervous system, and the endocrine system.

MacLean[6] conceptualizes the central nervous system as a triune brain, which developed its three parts rather separately in the course of evolution. These formations are the reptilian, the paleomammalian, and the neomammalian, and they differ markedly in chemistry and structure. The three parts function in a separate but highly interrelated and holistic way, and each part has the ability to be intelligent, sense time and space, remember, and influence motor functions. Each part probably also has its specific way of participating in the stress response. At this point it may be helpful to refer to Figure 4 for a diagram of the three anatomical areas of the brain.

The reptilian brain in mammals is primarily involved in self-preservation through such acts as territorial behavior, hunting, mating, and some social behaviors.

The brain stem, which includes the cerebellum, medulla, and pons, controls such basic needs and drives as metabolism and reproduction. The cerebellum is responsible for muscle coordination, the medulla controls heart and respiratory rate, and the pons relates to the autonomic nervous system.

The brain stem's reticular activating formation is important to the stress response, as you will read later. The reticular formation is a collection of diffuse neurons that occupies the mid-ventral portion of the medulla and midbrain and that regulates respiration, blood pressure, and heart rate. The reticular activating system (RAS) connects the brain stem, which contains the most basic body-regulating nerves, with the cortex, which is the area we use for our cognitive activities. In other words, the RAS connects the essence of the body and the essence of the mind because its nerve fibers travel from the brain stem and are very involved in electrical activity in the cortex. The RAS usually causes a generalized stimulation, but it can trigger specific reactions in

TRIUNE BRAIN

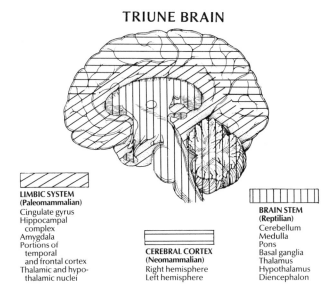

LIMBIC SYSTEM
(Paleomammalian)
Cingulate gyrus
Hippocampal
  complex
Amygdala
Portions of
  temporal
  and frontal cortex
Thalamic and hypo-
  thalamic nuclei

CEREBRAL CORTEX
(Neomammalian)
Right hemisphere
Left hemisphere

BRAIN STEM
(Reptilian)
Cerebellum
Medulla
Pons
Basal ganglia
Thalamus
Hypothalamus
Diencephalon

RETICULAR ACTIVATING SYSTEM

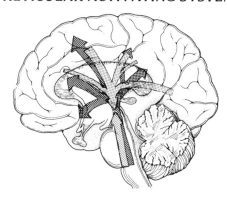

(Top)   Figure 4A: The triune brain as described by MacLean.

(Bottom) Figure 4B: The reticular activating system crosses anatomical boundaries and connects many parts of the brain from brain stem to cortex. (Adapted with permission from *The American Physiological Society.*)

the neocortex, such as by helping to focus our attention. Basically the RAS regulates alertness. It is most influential in determining whether we are awake, asleep, or somewhere in between these two states. The RAS also helps sort out stimuli for relevancy. For instance, if you are asleep, there may be many noises stimulating the brain, but the RAS may cause wakefulness only at certain sounds, such as your child's cry or a sudden, unusual noise. The RAS is able to activate our system at once if it determines a stimuli to be potentially harmful. Perhaps you've had the experience of waking very rapidly from a deep sleep in response to an unusual sound or a particularly frightening, vivid dream.

The RAS carries nerve impulses between the cortex and muscles and organs. It is an integrative system between the cortical and subcortical levels, and is important in stress responses. The cortex can activate the system to influence alertness so that we can experience an optimal state of arousal. A feedback loop exists so that the more stimulation fed into the RAS, the more excitement generated in the cortex, the muscles, and the autonomic nervous system. As you can see, it is possible for our arousal level to become too high or too constant. We can respond to stress by allowing too much stimulation into the feedback loop system. For instance, insomnia is highly likely if we go to bed while in a worried state (which causes both cortical and autonomic nervous system stimulation of the RAS) and having tight, achy muscles (which also causes stimulation of the RAS).

The diencephalon is the area of the brain stem that includes the basal ganglia, the thalamus, and the hypothalamus. The basal ganglia is highly complex and has much to do with regulating muscle tone throughout the body. The thalamus sorts nerve impulse signals and relays them to other appropriate areas of the brain. The hypothalamus, like the reticular activating system, plays a key role in our functional abilities generally, but is also highly important in our responses to stressors. The hypothalamus regulates the autonomic nervous system and the endocrine system. It controls such things as eating behaviors, gastrointestinal motility and secretion, body temperature, sexual behavior, and emotional behavior. The limbic system sends emotional stimulation to the hypothalamus, and the neocortex sends cognitively derived stimuli to it. The hypothalamus then uses these stimuli to signal the autonomic nervous system and the endocrine system to behave in certain ways. The hypothalamus controls the endocrine system by stimulating the pituitary gland, which specifically directs the endocrine glands. Direct stimulation is the route by which the hypothalamus influences both the sympathetic and parasympathetic branches of the autonomic nervous system.

The limbic system or paleomammalian brain is also very important to the understanding of the stress response. The limbic system and hypothalamus work closely together, and MacLean refers to this combination as the intermediate brain where instincts and affects are processed. The intermediate brain is responsible for regulating the basic drive systems of the brain and is the source of our emotions, gender identity, and senses of attachment and territoriality.

The limbic system itself consists of the cingulate gyrus, which influences sensorimotor association; the hippocampal complex, which is responsible for some auditory associations, as well as spatial mapping or knowledge of a territory (memory functions); and the amygdala. The amygdala heightens arousal of the hypothalamus if appropriate and is capable of stimulating almost any pattern of behavior. It also attaches values to sensory inputs so is crucial in the process of making judgments about whether something is rewarding or toxic. In this way it maintains our value systems by remembering the sensory input and their previous effects. Anatomically speaking, the limbic system includes parts of the temporal and frontal cortex and thalamic and hypothalamic nuclei. It is able to transmit our emotions to the cortical area and often helps us suppress one behavior and substitute a more appropriate behavior. For instance, we may become infuriated with a supervisor and have an unconscious impulse to attack him or her in a fit of rage. If our limbic system is working properly, we will abstain from attacking and substitute a behavior, such as talking, which may communicate our anger without disastrous consequences.

The third major area of the brain is the neocortex, or neomammalian brain. This is also called the higher, or integrative or associative cortex, and is where our higher level mental activities take place. The cortex is divided into right and left halves, which are connected by the corpus collosum, a rich network of nerves allowing communication between the right and left sides of the brain. Much attention has been given in recent years to the study of these two halves of the cortex. Generally, the left side of the cortex is thought to be involved in language and logical thinking, while the right side is used when we want to understand the wholeness of an object or situation. For instance, the right side of the brain is useful in reading maps, recognizing a face, and being able to enjoy or participate in art or music. The right side is also apparently the origin of primary process or the unconscious, where dreams and fantasies first form. The corpus collosum allows these kinds of stimuli to travel to the left side of the brain where they are processed into a verbalized form or are attended to with logic, such as trying to understand a dream. Logical, time-sequential thoughts are transmitted through the corpus collosum to the right side of the brain and from the right side are transmitted to the limbic system and hypothalamus, which, in turn, influence the autonomic nervous system and endocrine system. We can see, then, how our thoughts, our impressions of things, and our emotions can all influence the state of our body at any given time. This is a major piece of psychophysiologic information to recall when we discuss the stress response. You may want to refer to Figure 5 at this point for clarification of central nervous system interactions and for help in visualizing the following material on the autonomic nervous system and endocrine system.

The autonomic nervous system was once thought to be entirely involuntary or unable to be regulated. It is now clear that such things as gastrointestinal functioning, vascular conditions, metabolic rate, hormone balance, and some reproductive activities can be controlled by the kind of learning that takes place in biofeedback training. The autonomic nervous system is divided into the sympathetic nervous system and the parasympathetic nervous system. These two parts of the autonomic nervous system are not always opposing in function and may even work together occasionally. The sympathetic division is responsible for a general excitation effect, as in the fight or flight syndrome. It helps us tense the muscles of the gastrointestinal tract and of the vascular system and also activates the endocrine system. The parasympathetic nervous system is typically rather specific in its effect on the body. It is responsible for the relaxation of smooth muscle fibers, for decrease in the heart rate, and for an increase in gastrointestinal functioning, including salivation.

The endocrine system, like the nervous system, helps regulate various bodily activities by influencing other systems in the body to respond to the everchanging demands of the internal and external environment. The endocrine system is made up of many ductless glands that secrete hormones into the circulatory system. Organs with endocrine functions include the pituitary, pineal, thyroid, parathyroids, thymus, pancreas, spleen, kidneys, adrenals, and gonads. As was earlier stated, the hypothalamus signals the pituitary to release hormones, which signal other endocrine glands to release their hormones into the bloodstream. The hypothalamus influences both the cortex and the medulla of the adrenal gland. It stimulates the medulla directly through the sympathetic nervous system to release epinephrine into the system. It stimulates the cortex of the adrenals by signaling the pituitary to release the hormone ACTH. ACTH stimulates the adrenal cortex to release glucocorticoids, which increase metabolism, increase gluconeogenesis in the liver, and mobilize fats and proteins to enter the bloodstream. At the same time, mineralocorticoids are released from the adrenal cortex to cause the body to retain sodium and thus increase blood pressure and blood volume. The thyroid gland can be stimulated to release thyroxin, which increases the metabolic rate. Vasopressin may also be released by the posterior pituitary. Its function is to contract artery walls as an antidiuretic and thus increase the blood pressure.

The Stress Response

I want to emphasize again that the stress response is a very sensitive, normal, and protective mechanism that keeps us within a normal range of adaptation to our circumstances. Stressors are vital to our enjoyment of life.

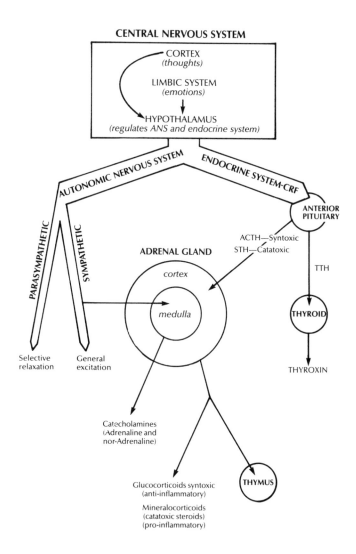

Figure 5: Schematic diagram of basic relationship of the central nervous system to the autonomic nervous system and the endocrine system.

They provide excitement and challenge and perhaps even offer clues to the meaning of our lives. Our stress mechanisms work best when the stressor that triggers a response is clear and can be dealt with quickly and effectively. If the stressor is ambiguous or fairly constant, we may experience no decisive relief from our stress response, and this pattern can easily lead to dis-ease or illness of some sort. Whether stressors are clear or ambiguous, it is important to remember that stressors do not automatically cause trouble and that we have basic control and choices about the effects of stressors in our lives. We can allow them to stimulate and challenge us or overwhelm us.

In this section, we will thoroughly examine Cannon's[7] work on acute stress and Selye's[8] work on more generalized long-term stress. The stress responses described by Cannon and Selye are different in autonomic nervous system pathways and in hormonal responses to these nervous system messages. Although each type of response can be elicited separately, during medium and intense states of arousal both the fight or flight arousal pattern and the general adaptation syndrome are activated simultaneously. If these systems are activated for too long a period and too intensely, one's health can be endangered. Throughout this section you are encouraged to refer to Figure 6 for a comparison of these two parts of the stress response.

The fight or flight syndrome, also called the defense reaction, involves the sympathetic nervous system and the adrenal-medullary system. When this system is activated, the animal or person becomes highly tense and alert in anticipation of some kind of confrontation. This fight or flight type of arousal was no doubt critical for survival in early man and in animals. For we who live in contemporary society, however, arousal into a state of

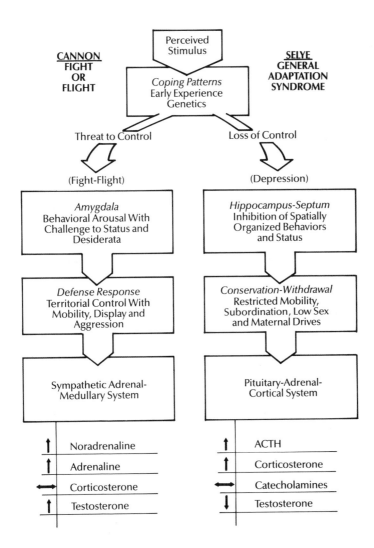

Figure 6: Conceptual model comparing the stress responses as described by Cannon and Selye. (Adapted with permission from *Springer-Verlag*, New York, Inc.)

wanting to fight or wanting to flee a situation is seldom useful and often harmful. Since our social norms mitigate against fighting or running from a situation, we are left with a physiologic arousal state and few really effective ways to regain a homeostatic balance without taking physical action.

Cannon long ago outlined the major features of the defense reaction or fight or flight arousal state. In the intervening years more details of how the defense system works have been gathered from psychophysiologic studies. Activation of the defense response seems to depend heavily upon the amygdala of the limbic system becoming stimulated by some threat to value associations already made. Neocortical influence may also play a part. An example of how this stimulation to the amygdala could occur is the simple one of perceiving a semi-trailer truck veering into your vehicle's lane of traffic at a high speed. This perception is registered perhaps both by the cortex and the amygdala, and value associations judge the situation to be a threat to life. These impulses in turn stimulate the posterior hypothalamus, which relays the message to the sympathetic nervous system. This same chain of central nervous system events occurs whenever there is a perceived threat of a psychosocial nature as well. For instance, if you are in a socially competitive situation, either for a new position at work, for more esteem in someone else's eyes, in some sports competition, or in a duel of wits, the neocortex and eventually the amygdala assess the situation as threatening to your status. The sympathetic nervous system will be aroused via the posterior hypothalamus. Besides primitive and obvious life-threatening situations and socially threatening situations, there is also an intrapsychic route for eliciting the defense reaction. Suddenly remembering after you are away from home that you left some-

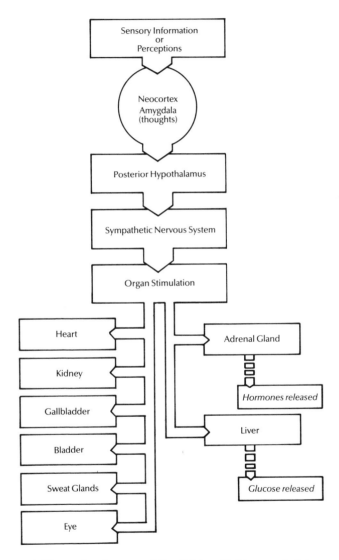

Figure 7: The major features of the fight or flight arousal state as described by Cannon.

thing cooking at high heat on the stove could elicit this reaction. Thinking of or dreaming of situations in which fear is elicited about one's own worth or competency or desirability or whatever can stimulate the sympathetic nervous system into a highly active state and elicit a fight or flight response.

What happens then, peripherally, after the sympathetic nervous system is activated? Figure 8 gives details of the autonomic nervous system effects on organs. Most notable is the reaction of the cardiovascular system. An increase in heart rate, in cardiac output, and in arterial blood pressure occurs. Blood is routed from the organs of digestion, the kidney, and the skin and supplied to the skeletal muscles. The sympathetic nervous system stimulates the medulla of the adrenal gland to produce the catecholamines epinephrine or adrenaline and norepinephrine or noradrenaline. Epinephrine signals the liver to release glycogen into the bloodstream as an energy source for the muscles. There is also an increase in the blood's ability to coagulate quickly in case of injury. Adrenaline has also been helpful in keeping the muscles from becoming quickly fatigued. Adrenaline and noradrenaline, which are very much alike in chemical structure, are both released during a defense reaction. Henry and Stephens[9] indicate that adrenaline output is increased during an event perceived as emotionally arousing, usually the emotion of fear. Noradrenaline is more often released when one is making an effort to achieve a goal and is associated most frequently with the emotion of irritation.

We have just seen the neuroendocrinology of Cannon's defense reaction and have noted various categories of perception of threat that trigger the fight or flight response. We will now investigate some details of how this response can lead to deleterious bodily effects if it

AUTONOMIC EFFECTS ON VARIOUS ORGANS OF THE BODY

Organs	Effect of Sympathetic Stimulation	Effect of Parasympathetic Stimulation
Eye		
Pupil	Dilated	Constricted
Ciliary muscle	Slight relaxation	Contracted
Sweat glands	Copious sweating (cholinergic)	None
Heart		
Muscle	Increased rate Increased force of contraction	Slowed rate Decreased force of atrial contraction
Coronaries	Dilated (β_2); constricted (α)	Dilated
Lungs		
Bronchi	Dilated	Constricted
Blood vessels	Mildly constricted	? Dilated
Gut		
Lumen	Decreased peristalsis and tone	Increased peristalsis and tone
Liver	Glucose released	Slight glycogen synthesis
Gallbladder and bile ducts	Relaxed	Contracted
Kidney	Decreased output	None
Penis	Ejaculation	Erection
Systemic blood vessels		
Abdominal	Constricted	None
Muscle	Constricted (adrenergic a) Dilated (adrenergic β) Dilated (cholinergic)	None
Skin	Constricted	None
Blood		
Coagulation	Increased	None
Glucose	Increased	None
Basal metabolism	Increased up to 100%	None
Adrenal cortical secretion	Increased	None
Mental activity	Increased	None
Skeletal muscle	Increased glycogenolysis Increased strength	None

Figure 8: Effects of autonomic nervous system on various organs of the body. (Adapted with permission from W. B. Saunders Company)

is prolonged. Since Cannon's defense reaction affects the cardiovascular system so intensely, one would expect that cardiovascular problems can arise from over-stimulation of this system.

During the fight or flight response, the sympathetic nervous system triggers vasoconstriction in small blood vessels. It also accelerates the heart rate and cardiac output, which increases arterial pressure. If the pressure inside the blood vessels continues, it is possible for the walls of the blood vessels to thicken, thereby narrowing even further the internal radius of the vessels. Eventually, hypertension results. Although there are many causes for this disease, it is often classified as a stress illness. It occurs in all ages and in both sexes. It is well-named the "silent killer" because people who are hypertensive are often asymptomatic.

Hypertension can cause diseases of the vascular system, the heart, and the kidneys. Friedman and Rosenman [10] describe vascular damage from hypertension in terms of a weakening or a tear in the artery lining. Cholesterol plaques may form at that point and further narrow the radius of the artery. If these plaques grow so much that they exceed the blood supply needed, they may decay and rupture. This can cause a clot and block the blood vessel entirely, causing a myocardial infarction or a stroke. It is also possible for generalized arteriosclerosis to develop so that blood flow is restricted to various degrees in many areas of the body. Again, as with hypertension, there are many causes for an arteriosclerotic process and hypertension is only one possibility.

Hypertension can also eventually cause heart disease by forcing the heart muscle to become thicker and heavier in an attempt to pump blood against more peripheral resistance. Finally, the heart muscle becomes dysfunctional, and congestive heart failure ensues. If the left ventricle becomes dysfunctional but the right ventricle continues pumping blood into the vessels in the lungs, pulmonary edema may result and eventually the liver, arms, and legs become edematous. Another way in which the heart is damaged from hypertension can be through myocardial infarction in which the plaques have built up in the coronary arteries and perhaps form a clot so that blood flow is shut off from one part of the heart muscle. This area then becomes necrotic or at least scar tissue forms, and the area becomes useless in participating in the pumping action required. A similar kind of process can occur in the vasculature of the kidneys causing tissue degeneration and dysfunction.

Henry and Stephens[11] report studies that demonstrate that the fight or flight sympathetic adrenal-medullary reaction disturbs lipid metabolism. An excess of free fatty acids can result from neural stimulation and from catecholamine responses. These free fatty acids can be converted by metabolic processes and deposited in the arterial walls causing atheroma.

It is now clear that stimulation from inner, psychosocial, and environmental sources can trigger Cannon's defense reaction, which influences mainly the cardiovascular system. If this sympathetic adrenal-medullary system is activated too intensely and/or too consistently, cardiovascular diseases such as heart disease, strokes, and related diseases such as gangrene and kidney problems can develop.

Some people react to stressors with a predominantly parasympathetic nervous system arousal. This kind of response is called *vagotonia.* Excitation of both the sympathetic and parasympathetic divisions of the autonomic nervous system can occur simultaneously. When stimulation of the parasympathetic system is strong, such stress reactions as nausea and shallow and irregular breathing can occur. More serious is the effect on slowing the heart and decreasing the force of the atrial beat which can lead to dizziness and fainting, low blood pressure, and even sudden death from the heart simply ceasing to beat.

Having examined in some detail the fight or flight stress response, we will now turn to the other part which is the general adaptation syndrome. Refer again to Figure 6 for a schematic comparison of these responses. As you can see, Selye's general adaptation syndrome involves activation of the pituitary-adrenal-cortical system and is associated with inhibition, withdrawal, and depression. Chronic arousal of this part of the stress response leads to many quite variant disease processes, such as Cushing's syndrome, dysfunction of the cardiovascular and immune systems, and stomach ulcerations.

Selye defines stress as the nonspecific response by the body to any demands made upon it, whether these are social, chemical, thermal, traumatic, or other sources. Selye first noticed the general adaptation syndrome when he observed clients who suffered from all kinds of disease processes and traumas had a basic quality about them of "just being sick."

The first phase of the general adaptation syndrome is an alarm reaction in which the body mobilizes in an attempt to adapt to the effect of the stressor (see Figure 9). During this time resistance drops so that we are more vulnerable to such reactions as shock and death. If the mobilization attempt is successful, the general resistance or ability to remain alive during the intense stress will increase and lead into the second stage, which is the stage of resistance. During this stage, the bodily alarm reaction signs have become unnoticeable and we seem to rise above normal in our resistance level. Also, our resistance to the specific stressor producing the general

GENERAL ADAPTATION SYNDROME

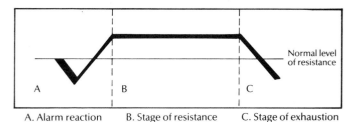

A. Alarm reaction   B. Stage of resistance   C. Stage of exhaustion

Figure 9: Title "The Three Phases of the General Adaptation Syndrome (GAS)" from STRESS WITHOUT DISTRESS by Hans Selye, MD (J.B. Lippincott, Publishers). Copyright © 1974 by Hans Selye, MD. Reprinted by permission of Harper & Row, Inc.

adaptation syndrome is at its highest level. Simultaneously, however, resistance to other stressors may tend to be·significantly lower than normal. You can see, then, that during the stage of resistance to one stressor we may be more vulnerable to the influence of a different type of stressor. Even if another type of stressor does not present itself at this time, the stage of resistance cannot last indefinitely. At some point, the stage of resistance gives way to the third stage, which is the stage of exhaustion. Selye says that exhaustion occurs because adaptation energy has been depleted. If there is no relief to the exhaustion so that a new supply of adaptation energy can be supplied, some of the signs of the alarm reaction reappear and death may ensue. During both the alarm reaction and the stage of exhaustion, corticoid activity can be very high and eventually will cause appearance of a typical triad of reactions, which include adrenal cortical enlargement, thymico-lymphatic atrophy and bleeding erosions of the gastrointestinal tract.

The general adaptation syndrome responds to both positive and negative stimuli. Reaction to negative stimuli is a state of distress, and reaction to positive stimuli is a state of eustress; however, a eustress state causes significantly less damage to the body than distress. Selye concludes that one's mental attitude plays a large part in determining whether adapting to change is successful or unsuccessful.

The general adaptation syndrome can vary widely in intensity. Obviously, we do not respond with the same intensity to suddenly feeling quite chilled by a cold breeze as we would to suddenly being confronted by someone who was pointing a gun in our direction. When the stressor triggers off an intense stress response, we can go through the alarm reaction, the stage of resistance, and the stage of exhaustion very rapidly.

Two serious consequences may result from the general adaptation syndrome. First, we may create many different forms of disease and wear and tear in our bodies as well as emotional and spiritual scars. Secondly, the more we use our reserves of adaptation energy, the more likely we are to hasten our death. There is no evidence that our basic deep reserves of energy for adaptation (aside from caloric intake kind of energy) can be restored. These deep reserves of adaptation energy may even be genetically programmed. In a superficial sense we can restore our energy for adaptation by adequate sleep, meditation, or deep relaxation exercises, but it is possible that we may never influence our level of basic adaptation energy. This, of course, makes the idea of preventing intense distress reactions highly desirable. You may want to think of your level of deep reserves of adaptation energy the next time you are tempted to fly into a fit of anger over some "small" issue or event. Ask yourself, "Do I really want to waste precious adaptation energy on this 'size' stressor?" Throughout the rest of this text, ideas concerning prevention of intense distress reactions will be presented.

Besides the general adaptation syndrome, Selye also describes the local adaptation syndrome. The local adaptation syndrome occurs in body tissues directly affected by a stressor, such as a chemical or a bacteria causing local inflammation. A local adaptation syndrome reacts specifically but, at the same time, because a stressor has impinged on the body, the general adaptation syndrome is triggered as well. Some of the hormones released during the general adaptation syndrome are of help in normalizing the area of local distress.

We will now look at the general adaptation syndrome in some detail and see a few of the more common results of this syndrome being called into play too often or too intensely. As we go into some detail on the hypothalamic-pituitary-adrenal-cortical axis portion of the stress response, remember that this is a description of the conservation-withdrawal behavior pattern. This behavior pattern is accompanied by feelings of helplessness, defeat, depression, failure, deprivation, or frustration. We experience this conservation-withdrawal reaction when we realize we have lost control and have relinquished ideas about regaining control. It is an uneasy acceptance of "the way it is" and contrasts with the experience of knowing we may be able to regain control, in which case the sympathetic-adrenal-medullary response is more likely to occur. If we apply this bit of neuroendocrinology to the work situation, we can see that people in a subordinate position who are not in charge of decision-making or policy-making could stay in a state of conservation-withdrawal. On the other hand, someone in a supervisory and power position who has a significant degree of control in the work situation would be more likely to experience a defense response involving the sympathetic-adrenal-medullary system we just discussed. It is interesting to note here that the Type

A people (impatient, aggressive, hurried), as defined by Friedman and Rosenman,[12] more often experience a defense response, while Type B people (patient, not achievement-oriented) are more familiar with a conservation-withdrawal response.

We will now trace the neuroendocrinologic response, as Selye describes it. First, the stressor affects some part of the nervous system, such as the cortex, the reticular activating system, or the limbic system (particularly the hippocampus and amygdala). The hypothalamus becomes stimulated from one or more of these sources and activates the autonomic nervous system to heighten vagal activity. The hypothalamus is also able to release CRF, or corticotropic hormone releasing factor, which stimulates the anterior lobe of the pituitary gland. The pituitary then releases three major hormones. First is thyrotropic hormone (TTH), which activates the thyroid gland and increases metabolism to help make energy more readily available during the stressful situation. Second is STH, or somatotrophic hormone, which is also called the growth hormone. This hormone travels to the cortex of the adrenal gland and helps release corticoids, in this case the catatoxic steroids such as aldosterone. The third major hormone released from the anterior pituitary is adrenocorticotropic hormone, or ACTH. This hormone also travels to the cortex of the adrenal gland and causes releases of corticoids, in this case syntoxic steroids such as cortisone. These syntoxic steroids travel to the thymus gland, which is responsible for production of white cells in the body and causes shrinkage of this gland. Refer to Figure 5 for a visual representation of this series of events.

The catatoxic steroids, which are also called proinflammatory, or mineralocorticoid, hormones, are important in the stress response since they launch an active attack on any invading substance. Somatotrophic hormone, aldosterone, and DOC, or desoxycorticosterone, are three catatoxic steroids. They increase the amount of inflamed tissue at a local site of injury to barricade off an aggressor such as a virus or a bacteria from entering the bloodstream. They also help destroy pathogens by signaling the liver to release enzymes.

The syntoxic steroids, such as ACTH, cortisone, and cortisol, are the other category of adaptive hormones. These hormones help us in a stressful situation to tolerate an intrusive substance by inhibiting an excessive defensive reaction. This enables a somewhat peaceful coexistence or passive tolerance of an invader. Their action decreases inflammation and the immune response. The syntoxic steroids are also called anti-inflammatory, or glucocorticoid, hormones. They induce glycogenesis for the quick energy necessary in a stressful situation.

We can see now how the conservation-withdrawal part of the stress response mobilizes and protects us during periods of dealing with stressors. What happens, though, when this response is overactivated? Physiologically, the adrenal glands enlarge, the thymus and lymph nodes shrink, the number of circulating eosinophil cells decreases, and the gastrointestinal tract produces ulcerations. Translated into disease categories, these become Cushing's syndrome, cardiovascular problems, immune system dysfunctions, and stomach ulcers. There are other possibilities, such as osteoporosis, caused by cortisone overproduction, which inhibits Vitamin D from bringing calcium into the blood for use in the bones. In this section, however, we will focus on the four major areas of disease process caused by the chronic malfunctioning of the general adaptation syndrome.

When considering that disease results from unsuccessful management of stressors, we must also keep in mind what Selye calls the conditioning factors, which are characteristics such as age, sex, diet, genetic predisposition and, I might add, ability to think rationally, perceive meaning and purpose in life, and socialize well, which can selectively exaggerate or inhibit the effects of stressors. This brings us back to our original position of appreciating stress and its management from a holistic point of view.

The first clear syndrome connected with an over-reactive conservation-withdrawal type of response is Cushing's syndrome, which is also called hyperadrenocorticism. This syndrome is characterized by a retention of salt and water in the body and by fat deposits on the back and abdominal walls, but not on the limbs. It occurs when ACTH becomes too easily imbalanced. Gifford and Gunderson [13] have collected extensive data that indicates that this disease occurs in some people as a result of the faulty grieving of a significant loss. Victims are vulnerable to depression and often have difficulties in personal relationships and personal identification. All of these psychosocial factors and more work together to contribute to a physiologic disturbance in the ACTH balance in the body.

Cardiovascular problems can also result from a malfunction of the general adaptation syndrome. For instance, mineralocorticoids influence salt balance, fluid retention, and renal damage, and overproduction leads to hypertension. Also, corticoids stimulate the release of renin in the kidney, which can cause an increase in blood pressure and can also lead to hypertension. As we have seen before in our discussion of hypertension, tears occur in the walls of arteries, plaques form, and an arteriosclerotic condition results, which can lead to strokes and myocardial infarctions. Selye has also noticed areas of myocardial necrosis in animals that were given a combination of glucocorticoid hormones and mineralocorticoid hormones and then exposed to a stressor. These animals invariably died from cardiac failure due to extensive necrosis without a prior coronary occlusion.

The third area adversely affected by chronic overactivation of the cortex of the adrenal gland is the immune system. If the catatoxic steroids are overproduced, there will be an exaggerated inflammation of tissue, usually in the nose and throat area, and this can develop into severe allergic reactions. On the other hand, if the syntoxic steroids are excessive, inflammation is prevented and we become more prone to bacterial and viral infections as well as the possibility of tumor growth. When syntoxic steroids are at a high level in the bloodstream, the thymus and the lymph nodes shrink, and the number of eosinophil cells decreases significantly. Eosinophils regulate allergic reactions to foreign substances by surrounding them, and so when their numbers decrease we are less well protected from noxious agents. Cortisone, a syntoxic steroid, besides shrinking the thymus and lymph nodes, can also decrease the ability of the lymphocytes and polymorphonuclear leukocytes to function. Cortisone also causes some inactivation of macrophages. These effects on our immune system at a cellular level also increase our overall vulnerability.

Another well-documented result of a malfunctioning general adaptation syndrome is gastrointestinal ulceration. Continuous stress increases hydrochloric acid secretion in the stomach in contrast to short-term stress, which decreases acid secretion. The heightened vagal activity, as directed by the hypothalamus, causes peptic ulceration. Also the stress hormones increase production of peptic enzymes which attack the stomach and intestinal lining.

Stress-Related Illnesses and Disorders

To be accurate, a list of stress-related illnesses and disorders should probably include anything that is not genetic in origin since almost any illness or disorder has a stress component. We have seen that Cannon's fight or flight response, when overused, can cause cardiovascular disorders. Derailment of Selye's general adaptation syndrome can cause illnesses such as Cushing's syndrome, cardiovascular disorders, immune system dysfunctions, and gastrointestinal ulcerations.

In this section we will examine a few more of the most prevalent and obvious stress-related problems. The first of these concerns muscle tension. During the fight or flight response, the adrenaline and noradrenaline influence motor nerves to cause tension in muscles as preparation for heightened activity. If this tensing reaction becomes chronic, muscle spasms develop. The result can be a great deal of fatigue, tension headaches, bruxism, temporomandibular joint pain, and pain along the spinal column, usually in cervical or lumbar areas.

Migraine headaches are another stress-related illness, although the causal factors can include diet, personality factors, and the inability to relax "evenly" without the erratic process of overworking, becoming exhausted, and then almost totally relaxing. During a fight or flight response the sympathetic nervous system reacts to cause vasoconstriction of the cranial arteries. Some people then apparently have a rebound effect from this and experience too great a degree of vasodilation, which causes a throbbing kind of pain usually located on one side of the head.

Like migraine headaches, the cause of rheumatoid arthritis is uncertain and there may be some genetic predisposition involved. Stressors, however, do seem to trigger the onset of this illness and influence its severity. An auto-immune reaction may be important here with stressors having affected the functioning of the immune system. Antibodies are apparently formed to mobilize against an inflamed synovial membrane of the joint but attack the membrane, too, causing it to replace its own cells too rapidly and to become swollen. Eventually the cartilage and joint may also be destroyed. The pain from this process may then induce tightening in the muscles, which adds secondary pain.

Selye contends that although the predispoisition to diabetes is inherited, a person's reaction to stressors can be a significant factor in whether or not the body will manifest this latent tendency. The blood sugar level can be raised when excessive amounts of adaptive hormones such as ACTH and STH are secreted. Blood sugar also rises when adrenaline from the fight or flight response signals the liver to release glycogen. Many or constant stressors and inadequate methods of handling them conceivably could lead, then, to a problem with diabetes.

Cancer is another disease considered by many as basically a problem of faulty immune protection due to hormonal influence of the immune system during distress. Like other disease processes we have mentioned, the cause of cancer is undoubtedly multifactorial and there is as yet no one precise pathway discovered which is the cause. LeShan[14] and others have defined cancer-prone personality factors as important in the etiology of this disease. LeShan describes the person who is prone to cancer as having patterns of suppressing feelings, holding in resentments, feeling isolated since very early in life from parents, and being prone to depression. We can see that these characteristics match some of the behavior patterns associated with the conservation-withdrawal reaction in which corticoids are perhaps at too high a level in the blood, thus causing a faulty immune reaction to aberrant cells in the body. What is puzzling is that tumor regression has occurred in some people under severe stress or while getting anti-inflammatory hormones such as ACTH or cortisone. Perhaps there is an optimal range for the corticosteroid level to support immunologic functioning and levels higher or lower than the optimal range might be suppressive.

At times it seems clear that there is a causal relationship between stressors and some physical disease patterns. Other physical disease patterns are related to stressors, but the exact pathway of causality is unclear. The question of the relationship of stressors to psychopathology such as high anxiety, affective disorders, and the psychoses is not answered at this time. As with other disorders, genetic predisposition may be an important factor. One problem is the assignment of meaning of the stressor to the person. Is the stress so "big" an event that nearly anyone would develop psychopathology? Or are there mental/emotional imbalances already present in the person that allow a maladaptive stress response to occur even to a "small" event and thus cause a psychopathological reaction? Why do some people who experience stressors lapse into a depression or even a psychotic episode while others learn from the distress experience and build even healthier mental/emotional coping patterns as a result of the experience? Investigating the relationship of stressors to psychopathology is a relatively new area of research in the stress field and so these questions cannot be answered definitively in this chapter.

Insomnia can certainly be a stress-related disorder. Both the central nervous system and the endocrine system can be involved. You will remember that during the general adaptation syndrome the hypothalamus stimulates the anterior pituitary to secrete various hormones.

One of these is thyrotropic hormone. This hormone goes to the thyroid gland and causes release of thyroxin in high levels during a stress response. Thyroxin heightens the metabolic rate of the body at times to a degree which makes falling asleep very difficult. The hypothalamus also influences the reticular activating system which is basically responsible for our degree of wakefulness. Feedback loops exist between the cerebral cortex of the brain and the reticular activating system as well as between our muscles and the reticular activating system. Insomnia then can be caused by an increase in activity in the cerebral cortex as when we are worrying about problems. This increases activity in the reticular activating system and stimulates wakefulness. Also, if our muscles are very tense this information will be relayed to the reticular activating system and we will experience wakefulness rather than sleepiness.

The behavior disorder of accident-proneness is, in most cases, very clearly related to either the individual's general level of distress or to his or her condition immediately after experiencing a stressor. Some of the problem of accident-proneness may come from neurohormonal imbalances in the body and some may be due simply to a preoccupation with a stressor rather than one's immediate activity.

Addictions are a familiar way to handle stress. We may be addicted to certain types of food, to tobacco, caffeine and/or alcohol and drugs. Some people are even addicted to such stress reducers as watching television or being in the presence of a certain person. The types of objects to which we become addicted in our attempts to comfort our distress or heighten our eustress is probably unlimited. Basic to all these addictions is the fact that a person is ill-equipped to handle stressors effectively without the use of these substances, objects, people or events. Trouble begins when the object of addiction, such as alcohol or fattening foods, becomes hazardous to our health. Also, a secondary stress response is set up when we realize the harmfulness or inadequacy or distastefulness of our addiction and do not discontinue the addiction behavior. Often addictions go unnoticed until someone else points out the addictive pattern. Ideally, we can all effectively utilize various objects and situations to allay our distress or enhance our eustress without becoming limited to certain types of relief or enhancement and thus becoming dependent on them and losing our own personal sense of control.

In this chapter we have examined closely our mind/ body in neuroendocrinological terms. We have also studied details of the stress response and have surveyed the relationship of stress reactions and many disease processes. The rest of this text will be devoted to preventing intense stress responses and to managing them well if they should happen to occur.

REFERENCES

1. Green, E., and Green, A. *Beyond Biofeedback*. New York: Dell Publishing Co., Inc., 1978.

2. Capra. F. *The Tao of Physics*. Berkeley: Shambhala, 1975.

3. LeShan, L. *The Medium, the Mystic, and the Physicist*. New York: Ballentine Books, 1975.

4. Pribram, K. H. "What the Fuss Is All About." *Re-Vision*, Summer/Fall 1978, pp. 14-18.

5. Bohm, D. "The Enfolding-Unfolding Universe." *Re-Vision*, Summer/Fall 1978, pp. 24-51.

6. MacLean, P.D. "Sensory and Perceptive Factors in Emotional Functions of the Triune Brain." *Biological Foundations of Psychiatry*, Vol. 1, ed. R. G. Grenell and S. Gabay. New York: Raven, 1976.

7. Cannon, W. B. *Bodily Changes in Pain, Hunger, Fear, and Rage.* 2nd. ed. Boston: Charles T. Branford Co., 1953.

8. Selye, H. *Stress Without Distress.* New York: The New American Library, Inc., 1975; *Stress in Health and Disease.* Reading, MA: Butterworths, 1976; *The Stress of Life.* Rev. ed. New York: McGraw-Hill Book Co., 1978.

9. Henry, J. P., and Stephens, P. M. *Stress, Health, and the Social Environment.* New York: Springer-Verlag, 1977.

10. Friedman, M., and Rosenman, R. H. *Type A Behavior and Your Heart.* Greenwich, CT: Fawcett Publications, Inc., 1974.

11. Henry, J. P., and Stephens, P. M. *Stress, Health, and the Social Environment.* New York: Springer-Verlag, 1977.

12. Friedman, M., and Rosenman, R. H. *Type A Behavior and Your Heart.* Greenwich, CT: Fawcett Publications, Inc., 1974.

13. Gifford, S., and Gunderson, J. G. "Cushing's Disease As a Psychosomatic Disorder: A Selective Review of the Clinical and Experimental Literature and a Report of Ten Cases." *Perspectives of Biological Medicine*, 1970, *13*, 169-221.

14. LeShan, L. *You Can Fight for your Life.* New York: M. Evans and Company, Inc., 1977.

CHAPTER 3

Stress and the Environment

Our environment is one of the personal mediating factors identified in Chapter One as a source of stressors. By environment, I refer to our external surroundings—what is outside our skin. Our environment may be thought of in two general categories:

1. Physical aspects: location, surroundings, home and work settings.
2. Social aspects: the people with whom we spend time and energy.

A simple example of a physical environmental factor is the weather. Most of us handle stress better when the sun is shining and the temperature and humidity are moderate than on cold, damp, rainy days or in one-hundred-degree heat. Similarly, if our social environment contains positive, supportive people, our ability to deal with stress is greater than it is if our social environment is cluttered with many negative, unpleasant people. Identification with a group actually helps people avoid stress illnesses, while dysfunctional social interactions lead to mental and emotional reactions, stress responses, and then to disease. The Roseto community, which is discussed later in this chapter, is an example of a group that was able to help its members allay stress problems. At the other end of the scale are people who do not have contact with others or do not maintain a meaningful sense of group membership and have, therefore, placed themselves at higher risk for accidents, respiratory diseases, suicide, and schizophrenia.[1]

While it is true that most stress from environmental factors can be diminished or prevented by changing our attitudes toward elements of our environment, there arises an important question. Why expend time and energy on attitude changes when we can re-shape the environment in simple ways that will lower the number or intensity of stressors we must cope with?

Obviously, one's ability to control environmental factors ranges from no significant control to almost total control. Environmental conditions over which we have little control are such things as earthquakes and the views of people who are extremely dogmatic. We can exert more control over such environmental elements as the amount of noise in the immediate area and the attitude of a reasonable person toward us. Those things we have almost total control over include the cleanliness and order of our own home and whether or not we choose to spend time with certain individuals.

Accurately assessing our ability to control any given environmental stressor is important to prevent the stress of trying to change those things over which we have almost no control or giving up too soon on those things over which we have almost total control. When you finish your assessment, you can decide whether to move forward to change a factor, retreat from it, or stay with it and change your attitude toward it if you wish.

In this chapter, physical environment includes our planet, our country, your community, and your personal everyday physical spaces. Social environment refers to your national and international membership in the human social sphere as well as your community affiliations and your personal circle of family and friends. The following two sections of this chapter will present guidelines to help you assess your physical and social environments. We will then explore possibilities for changing some facets of both of these aspects of your environment to enable you to reduce the number and/or intensity of stressors impinging upon you in daily life.

Assessing Your Physical Environment

The purpose of this section is to help you become more acutely aware of the environmental stressors that have some kind of impact on you daily. Often we accommodate to the stressful parts of our physical environment either without thinking or by assuming these stressors could not be changed. Actual accommodation to an environmental stressor is possible, of course, but sometimes we have simply learned to "put up with" stressors and have suppressed our real feelings rather than actually having attained a stress-free accommodation.

Take a minute now to list five things in your physical environment to which you know you react in a stressful way. Then list five features of your environment to which you react with an invigorated and/or relaxed feeling. When you have finished your list, keep it near for reference.

Here are some questions to consider before you work with your list again. What is stressful to you as a planetary citizen? Are you distressed about the ecological state of our world-wide environment such as air pollution, the destruction of natural resources, and the reduction of our ozone layer? Do you worry about how pollution of our air, water, and food are affecting you?

Let us focus on your immediate physical environment such as the climate in which you live, the degree and types of pollution you live with, the availability of community services, and the safety of your environment. What is the climate like where you live in terms of altitude, seasonal changes in temperature and humidity, and the number of days of sunshine you experience each year? Do you actually enjoy this aspect of your physical environment or do you find yourself putting up with it or complaining about it as a stressor in your life? Have you always wanted to live somewhere else? Have you actually investigated other less stressful climates? If you live in an area that has seasons, do you change your schedule with the seasons, or at least aim for a slightly hibernative level of activity in the winter? Do you pay attention to the time when the sun rises and sets and gear any of your activities to be in tune with the sun?

What types of pollution do you encounter daily that are stressful to you? Do you worry about the effects of radiation on your immediate environment? Do you experience noise pollution to such a degree that it interferes with your cognitive processes and emotional stability? (Familiar forms of noise pollution are jackhammers and adolescents with stereos!) Are you concerned about chemical pollutants in our soaps, shampoos, deodorants, makeup, and food? Do smoke-filled rooms cause you distress? Do you respond to pollutants with allergic reactions that are themselves stressful?

Another environmental consideration is the stress created or prevented by the availability of community services. Are you satisfied or stressed by how the garbage is collected and the streets are cleaned and repaired? Is public transportation a help or hindrance to you? How much stress is involved in procuring food and other materials in your community?

Safety is another basic aspect of the environment and also influences our stress levels. Are you free from constant worry about disease, accidents, and death? Have you kept your environment free of fire hazards, of the likelihood of falling, and of being accidentally poisoned? Take a mental and visual inventory right now of your home and work environments to evaluate the safety factors of each of these areas.

Many personal aspects of our environment are easily within our control. Again, the key is to become aware of possible stressors so that you can change them if you wish. For example, part of our external environment is the food we eat. Are you pleased with the quantity and quality of the food you eat or is there some distress in relating to this part of your environment?

Clothing is another very important source of distress or satisfaction. Does anything about your clothing distress you? Are the sizes and styles comfortable for you? Are the colors and kinds of fabric comfortable? It is important to remember that synthetic fabrics stop the air from flowing through them and thus lead to overheating, perspiring, and creating an imbalance of the skin bacteria. Natural fabrics, such as silks, cotton, and wool, avoid this problem.

Now let us assess some of the more aesthetic details of the various physical spaces you use on a daily or weekly basis. First, visualize the rooms or other spaces that fall in this category. Perhaps these will be such spaces as your bedroom, your kitchen, your family room, your car, and your office. Ask yourself about each of these spaces. Is each large enough or am I under some distress from being in a space that is too small? Is my use of each space satisfactory? For instance, have I designed these living and working areas to allow myself privacy and to allow myself an opportunity to do specific rewarding things, such as exercising? Can I enter and leave each space freely? Can I relax in each space? What meaning does each space have to me? Do these meanings create distress or relaxation? Is the furniture comfortable in each space? Think about the amount of time you spend in your bed and your office chair. If you spend most of your workday on your feet, perhaps more relevant is the comfort of your shoes.

Another important dimension in evaluating your physical environment is color as you utilize and experience it. The colors of rooms, the colors used in clothing, and even the colors of the food you eat are important factors in your environment. Much research has been done on the relationship of color and human behavior. Besides general personal preferences for colors gained from our experiences with them throughout our lives, we also learn to associate specific colors with certain moods or thoughts. The effect of different colors on us can also be observed from a physicist's point of view, since each color has its own wavelength and thus its own energy along the light energy spectrum. Whatever the reasons for responding to some colors with rage or agitation and to other colors with relaxation and a mellow feeling, thoughtful choices about color in our lives seems to be an important factor in managing stress.

To build your awareness of the effects of various colors on you, try sitting quietly with a color chart that exposes only one color at a time. Close your eyes and let your body relax and your mind clear, then open your eyes and look directly at the color you are testing and notice what feeling or reaction you are aware of to that color. You may want to make a note of that reaction and try the process again on some other day at a different time of day to see if this reaction is consistent. A simple way to test your response to the colors in your life is to sit in your office or at home and test the colors of the walls and furnishings one at a time.

A final query about your physical environment is, "Does my environment bring me closer to or farther away from nature?" Suppose you live in a city high-rise apartment and walk a few blocks on the concrete sidewalk to another high-rise office building or to a hospital to spend the day and then proceed by taxi to a restaurant for the evening. You probably will have less ability to manage stress than someone who has spent the day gardening. Many of us crave the relaxation and attunement with nature that can occur through trips to such places as the beach or the mountains. Many vigorous people in their 80s and 90s report that their ability to cope well with life is attributable in part to their devotion to their vegetable and flower gardens. Think for a moment about the time you spend with nature that is relaxing and fulfilling for you. Do you include adequate time in this part of your environment every day, every week, and every year?

At this point, retrieve the list you started at the beginning of the chapter, and add five more factors in your physical environment that may be causing stress. Then list five more things that you find relaxing and revitalizing about your physical environment. Save this list to use again in the section on management of your physical environment.

Assessing Your Social Environment

Before you continue, make a list of five socially stress-ful situations in your current life and five social situa-tions that you find relaxing and pleasant.

Our modern communications systems makes each one of us planetary neighbors. How much distress do you acquire from seeing and hearing about wars and natural disasters around the world? Do you worry about the stability of world peace? Are you at ease about how the many cultures of the world are sharing their knowl-edge and resources? How do you react to economic conditions and the current crime rate abroad? Do elect-ed officials increase or decrease your stress level?

Does the social milieu of your community create or prevent stress? Does your community accept many life-styles or can only certain "types" of people live there? Do you worry about drug and alcohol abuse in your area? Do you feel you must compete with the neighbors to acquire material goods such as clothing, cars, and a larger house? Do you consider your neighbors to be helpful and supportive of one another?

On a more personal level, let's look at two specific ways to determine the social sources of environmental stress in your life.

First is a scale to measure the impact of life event changes on you. Second is systems theory as a frame-work for understanding social stressors. The Holmes and Rahe Social Readjustment Rating Scale (SRRS), shown on pages 74-75, is one tool to measure the effect of social changes on your life. You will notice that 43 life events are listed, each with a corresponding mean value.

To use this rating scale, read each life event, word, or phrase, and if this applies to you within the past year, record the mean value score for that item. When you have finished the checklist, total your score. A score less than 150 is associated with a 30% chance of serious illness. A score of 150-299 indicates approximately a 50% chance of a serious illness developing. If your score is above 300, you have approximately a 90% chance of becoming seriously ill in the next two years. These percentages are rough guesses, and obviously the chance of illness decreases as your ability to manage stress increases. A word of caution is appropriate here. Take care to avoid thinking that a high score automatically means you will become ill. Rather, use the information to gain some perspective on the number of changes you have gone through this past year and the possible effect on your health. You then will be in a stronger position to deal with potential problems.

Much research is being conducted on the subject of life events and illness. Fairbank and Hough[2] report a study of categories of life change events. They found that undesirable events stemming from possible inferior social functioning, though the events were within the subject's control, were associated with illness. After systematically comparing 23 methods of weighing life events in terms of how well they predicted psychiatric symptomatology, Ross and Mirowsky[3] concluded that the highest undesirability of event score predicts symptoms better than change in event scores. The perfect life event-illness correlation tool has yet to be developed. That is why the SRRS, though frequently utilized, is best viewed as a helpful but not absolutely predictive tool.

The SRRS gives you some information about social events over the past year and your likelihood of illness in the future. Let's turn now to the use of social systems

THE SOCIAL READJUSTMENT RATING SCALE*

Life Event	Mean Value
1. Death of spouse	100
2. Divorce	73
3. Marital separation	65
4. Jail term	63
5. Death of close family member	63
6. Personal injury or illness	53
7. Marriage	50
8. Fired at work	47
9. Marital reconciliation	45
10. Retirement	45
11. Change in health of family member	44
12. Pregnancy	40
13. Sex difficulties	39
14. Gain of new family member	39
15. Business readjustment	39
16. Change in financial state	38
17. Death of close friend	37
18. Change to different line of work	36
19. Change in number of arguments with spouse	35
20. Mortgage or loan for major purchase (home, etc.)	31
21. Foreclosure of mortgage or loan	30
22. Change in responsibilities at work	29

Life Event	Mean Value
23. Son or daughter leaving home	29
24. Trouble with in-laws	29
25. Outstanding personal achievement	28
26. Wife begin or stop work	26
27. Begin or end school	26
28. Change in living conditions	25
29. Revision of personal habits	24
30. Trouble with boss	23
31. Change in work hours or conditions	20
32. Change in residence	20
33. Change in schools	20
34. Change in recreation	19
35. Change in church activities	19
36. Change in social activities	18
37. Mortgage or loan for lesser purchase (car, TV, etc.)	17
38. Change in sleeping habits	16
39. Change in number of family get-togethers	15
40. Change in eating habits	15
41. Vacation	13
42. Christmas	12
43. Minor violations of the law	11

*See Holmes, T. H. and Rahe, R. H.: The Social Readjustment Rating Scale, *Journal of Psychosomatic Research 11:*213-218, 1967. Pergamon Press, Elmsford, NY 10523. *Reprinted with permission.*

theory to analyze your current social relationships and assess them for their impact on your level of stress.

Social systems theory provides a way to look at our relationships with others, understand them, and do something to change the relationships that cause distress. Social systems theory is derived from general systems theory. Berrien[4] finds analogies among all natural systems, such as chemomechanical, electrical, biological, psychological, and social systems. In order to utilize systems theory, let us first become familiar with the terms as defined by Berrien. You may want to refer to Figure 10 as you read each definition to help you visualize systems theory as it applies to social interaction.

System: a set of components interacting with one another in a boundary that selects both the kind and rate of flow of inputs and outputs to and from the system.

Component: a unit of a system that in combination with other units functions to combine, separate, or compare the inputs to produce outputs.

Boundary: a region separating one system from another whose function is to filter or select inputs and outputs. It can be distinguished by some difference in the relationships existing among the components within the boundary compared with relationships which occur across the boundary.

Inputs: energies (or information) absorbed by the system. There are two kinds of inputs. First are maintenance inputs, which are those that prepare or maintain the system to function. Second are signal inputs.

SOCIAL SYSTEM MODEL

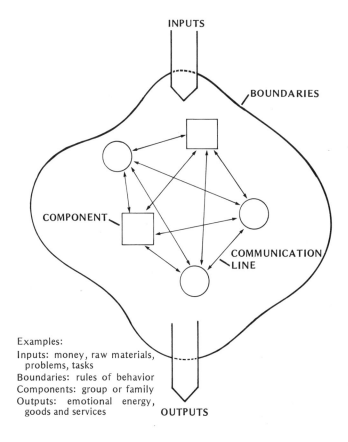

Figure 10: A social system model which applies general systems theory to social interaction.

These inputs are processed by the system.

Outputs: those energies or information or products
             that are expelled by the system as a conse-
             quence of its operation and are different
             in some significant way from inputs.

Before you read further, think for a moment about
your family system, your work system, and any other
social systems to which you belong. Keep these systems
in mind as you learn more now about how systems function.

Figure 11 illustrates three types of social systems. As
you can see, it is possible for people to be too close and
form what Bowen calls an "undifferentiated ego mass"[5]
or to be too distant and have a disintegrated system.
Each of these fosters little growth. The most productive
system is the one in which contact is made but individuals remain differentiated from one another. In this
system growth occurs with little distress.

One social system relates to others, and subsystems
can form within a larger system. Some subsystems form
triads or triangles, and are usually stressful because two
people are typically closer to each other than to the
third person at any given time. Which two people are
closest to each other can vary. Occasionally two people
in a triad will become negative toward the third. This is
one example of the scapegoat phenomenon.

In a social system many patterns develop to maintain homeostasis so that stress from change can be
avoided. This is true even if the stress would be minor
and temporary and would lead to less stress in the future. In the interest of homeostasis a system may lose
flexibility. Those in charge may demand that the rules
be followed as an attempt to keep behavior predictable
and representative of that particular system.

TYPES OF SOCIAL SYSTEMS

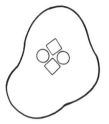

UNDIFFERENTIATED EGO MASS
Individuals have unclear boundaries but cannot own thoughts and feelings as separate from others' thoughts and feelings. Rarely any growth occurs.

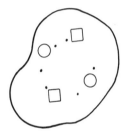

DISINTEGRATED
Boundaries are clear but little contact is maintained among members who stay together as a system but do not support each other to grow.

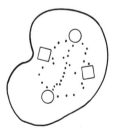

GROWTH PRODUCING
Boundaries are clear but individuals retain emotional and cognitive contact. Each member is free to grow and change with little resistance from the system.

Figure 11: A comparison of three types of social systems.

Rules and inputs largely determine what *roles* people will play with one another in any given system. In some instances people will try to play the same role no matter what system they join. No matter how the roles are established, however, the system will organize toward keeping the same people playing the same roles.

Reciprocity is an important systems concept. Reciprocity means that change in one part of the system is followed by somewhat equal and opposite change in another part of it. Bowen speaks of the overfunction-dysfunction reciprocating mechanism.[6] If one member of a system gets too distressed and does not play his or her role well, another member is likely to come to the rescue and compensate by being superfunctional. Although this keeps the system in a homeostatic state, the distress cost is high for both members of the reciprocity.

Roles can be conceptualized in three ways. First, in a generic sense, roles are determined by age, sex, and length of time in the system. In a family, for instance, the oldest child usually takes quite a different role in the family than does the youngest child. A second way to categorize roles is by task. At the workplace, for instance, a supervisory role is different in many ways from that of the person being supervised. A great deal of distress can be generated when people do not play these roles as others expect them to.

A third way to view roles within a system is to note what affective or feeling roles people take. Virginia Satir[7] has identified five affective roles that people typically play in families. These are easily played in other social systems as well.

First is the person who placates or agrees with others and wants to please them. This person often gives the message of being helpless and feels worthless much of the time.

The second is the person who blames. This person is a faultfinder who can point out your past, present, and even future faults with ease. This person is trying to establish him or herself as "the one who knows" and wants to be obeyed. His or her voice is often very loud and sharp. The person who is critical of others suffers a great deal from self-criticism.

The third affective role is that of a person who acts like a computer, being ultra-reasonable and very calm on the outside. In the process of suppressing his or her feelings, the computer personality's voice becomes a monotone and the internal experience can be that of vulnerability in spite of the external appearance.

The fourth affective role is that of the distractor. This person responds to others in ways that make little sense. His or her comments are irrelevant, and, of course, it is very hard to get this person to respond directly to a specific question or comment. The internal experience a person has when playing this role is that of purposelessness and loneliness.

The fifth affective role is that of leveling or congruence. It contrasts with the first four in that it is a healthy stance to take in a social situation. This person is an asset to any social system. He or she is not easily threatened because healthy self-esteem makes it easy to form and maintain relationships. This person's words, voice, facial expression, and general body language all give the same message at the same time, thus making it easy for people to understand and trust this person. There is a feeling of integration, openness, and aliveness about the congruent person which is powerful and tends to influence others in a social system to cling less to their unhealthy roles and become more congruent internally.

Each of us has no difficulty enacting any of these roles. We have all played them at some point in our lives as members of social systems. Hopefully we spend most of our time in the last role. The next best option for the sake of the individual and the social system is that people be able to slide from one role to another at various times. The least satisfactory option is that a person gets stuck in one of the four troublesome affective roles and is unable or unwilling to move out of that role. This influences the entire system to become more rigid.

Now take some time to apply what you have just learned about the theory of social systems to your interactions with your social environment. The purpose of this exercise is to help you discover and clarify details about what is gratifying and what is distressing in your relationships within your social environment. You may want to consider the following possible groups as your social systems:

- your family of origin, even if you no longer live geographically close to them.
- your present family or people you live with.
- various systems and subsystems at your work place.
- your community or neighborhood group memberships, formal and informal.

To gain the greatest rewards from this process, make a sketch right now of each of your major social systems. Refer to Figure 10 again as a model for your sketches.

As you look at each of your drawings, ask yourself the following questions (and any of your own, of course). Pay close attention to your body as you are doing this. Watch for physiological signs of relaxation or distress as reactions to your analysis of each system. You may find yourself smiling and letting go of tension in muscles or you may find yourself suffering such distress signs as mild stomach cramps, headache, or tachycardia. Use the following list of questions as a guideline for your assessment process.

- How many components or members belong to the system?
- Is this number comfortable for you or do you get too much or too little attention?
- Are you in a reciprocal relationship with one or more people in the system so that when one of you overfunctions the other becomes dysfunctional?
- What generic role do you have in the system?
- What instrumental role do you play in the system?
- Do you usually play the role of placater, blamer, computer, distractor, or leveler in the system?
- What do you do to help maintain system homeostasis rather than allow change to occur in the system?
- What are some of the most prevalent rules or norms of the system?
- Are the rules or boundaries of the system so strong that breaking them would lead to rejection of a member?
- Is the system an undifferentiated ego mass, a disintegrated system, or a growth-producing one?
- What problems does this system try to solve?
- What tasks does the system perform?
- What does the system require to maintain itself?
- What does the system produce as outputs?
- Is the system working efficiently?
- Is the system operating as you want it to operate

so that you experience minimum distress and maximum pleasure?

When you finish your assessment of each system with which you are involved, notice any similarities or differences among the systems. Do you have a pattern of selecting certain kinds of systems? Do you play a similar kind of role in each system? For instance, do you consistently struggle for power or influence or do you typically take a passive role?

Hopefully, you now have several new or clarified insights into how you usually behave as a member of a social system. We will now take a look at the context of your social environment from a wider, more general point of view. In this assessment you are asked to think in terms of energy loss and gain. Look at Figure 12, which shows a method for rating the energy dynamics involved in relating to various people and events in your life. To use this rating form, simply jot down, in whatever order they occur to you, 10 energy-draining and 10 energizing people or events in the appropriate columns. Then score each item from 1 to 5 to indicate the degree of intensity this item holds for you. When you have finished rating each item, total the numbers in each column. This figure will give you a rough estimate of how many energy units you are losing and how many units you are gaining from your general life situation. To be even more precise you would have to determine how many times each of these items occurs within a certain time frame. You may want to extend your list beyond 10 items to help you gain more awareness of how you are using your energy.

Now retrieve your earlier list of five relaxing and five distressing elements of your social environment. Add at least five more items to each list from the assess-

ENERGY RATING SCALE

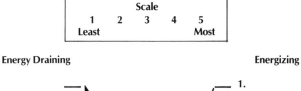

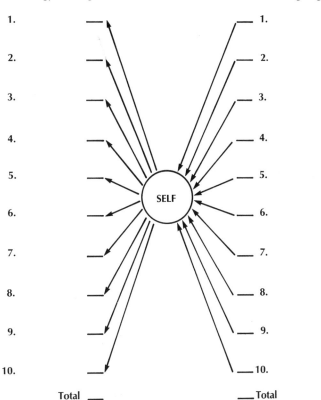

Figure 12: Rating scale for energizing and energy draining relationships and activities.

ment work you have just done on your social environment. Save this list for use when we discuss managing the stressors which originate in your social environment.

Managing Your Physical Environment

When you were assessing your physical environment from a world, national, community, and personal perspective, you may have noticed that there were thousands of possibilities for the physical environment to induce distress. It is possible to feel overwhelmed by the sheer number of stressors and assume that the physical environment is simply out of our control. When this happens we are much more likely to try to accommodate to a less than comfortable environment rather than take action to restore or rearrange our surroundings. While it is wonderful that we have the capacity to accommodate to our environment and that this ability is probably even lifesaving at times, most of us in accommodating probably settle for less than we have to.

We have already noticed that Earth is actually in many ways very small and all of us are connected; therefore, anything that we can do to influence the physical environment at a national and international level will in some way affect our degree of stress. Let's take a look at the areas of ecology and political action as arenas in which to place energy for a positive influence on our environment in a large-scale sense.

One ecological principle to consider is how to live our lives so that we can avoid distress to ourselves and to our planet. This means adopting a philosophy that allows our needs to be simple so that we buy to fill simple needs rather than buy in excess and discard what we do not need.

We could learn much from the American Indians

in this respect, many of whom conceptualize the earth as an organism or living being, a "gigantic body of a conscious, struggling, living being."[8] Whatever the belief, it is a universal experience to feel a reduction in distress when tuning in to nature. It makes sense, then, to do our part to keep our earth healthy enough to support us well and to enable us to feel peaceful when we contemplate it.

Can you think of ways to simplify your needs so that you will consume fewer of the earth's limited resources? You might look for changes in food buying, food preparation, transportation, housing, buying consumer goods for yourself and others, clothing, and recreation, to name a few. Joining an ecology group can be a positive way to help maintain our environment as a source of pleasure rather than distress. Groups such as the Sierra Club, Environmental Action, and Solar Lobby[9] are concerned with such issues as saving rain forests, protecting wildlife, and funding solar energy development.

On a community and personal level of interacting with the environment, you may ask the question, "How can I improve my environment and thus save myself from secreting too much adrenaline and too many catecholamines?" At a community level there are many considerations for taking action to relieve distress. You may decide to move to a new community. This would be a consideration, of course, if you evaluated your community as being unsafe—a place where there is an inordinate risk of being robbed, assaulted, or polluted to death. Convenience factors are also important for lowering levels of distress. If you live in an area with inadequate transportation, is there a way to organize a community cooperative effort for transporting yourself to and from work and doing errands? A cooperative community effort may also be necessary to maintain or create a visually attractive environment. For instance, community members may want to cooperate in resisting a change in zoning if these laws present a threat to the maintenance of pleasant open spaces.

Now let's take a look at ways to manage your personal environment so you can save your adaptation energy for more important issues. A large part of personal environmental influence is the climate, as we noted earlier. If the climate in your area seems to lead to a great deal of discomfort or illness, consider moving to another area. Check out your reasons for not moving to be sure that you are not stuck in some unproductive habit patterns or reacting to fear of change at the thought of moving. When people are convinced that their health and well-being are at stake, arrangements to move to a more suitable climate can usually be made.

Often people will not adapt successfully to a climate because they do not dress appropriately. In the winter months, for instance, women may wear a fashionable style of shoe which may have an open toe and a very high heel, all the while complaining about how miserably cold it is outdoors. If you wish to cut down on your distress level by dressing appropriately for the weather, try developing a very strong conscious intent to be comfortably dressed. Notice how this intent may change both your dressing and clothes-buying habits. You may also want to develop a similar intent for yourself about being comfortable in your home and office. Action may come in the form of repairs, increased insulation measures, and in the development of solar heating and cooling systems so that greater comfort can be maintained without destroying natural resources in the process.

Another very important area to consider is that of

avoiding accidents. Routine inspection of work and home for safety hazards is certainly an important way to prevent a stressful, dangerous incident. The more difficult part is completing repairs or changing defects that might be dangerous. Most people avoid home repairs for as long as possible, but then live with the distress of the unfinished job. We all realize, too, that keeping property in good working condition will help avoid chronic irritations that accompany such things as a leaky faucet, a sluggish drain, or squeaking door hinge. Another habit that requires discipline to develop is that of keeping our environment organized so that we can avoid the frustration of searching for items we have misplaced and of having the sense that we live in utter chaos.

Perhaps when you were assessing your physical environment at home and at work you realized that you have been living in a situation which could be defined as overcrowded—that situation in which you feel that you cannot manage to be alone whether for thinking, meditation, exercise, painting, or whatever. It is usually possible even in a large family group to delineate some territory which is private or at least can be made private on a consistent basis during certain hours of the day.

Having one's own space defined may be related to wanting some quiet time alone. You will recall from Chapter Two that whatever we perceive as noise stimulates our reticular activating system and leads to sympathetic nervous system activity which is part of being stressed. Some noises, of course, can actually cause tissue damage and increased blood pressure along with other distressing effects. The quality and the meaning to us of sound can be felt as a stressor. For instance, we can be interrupted by even a soft, low-pitched sound, but if we are concentrating we may experience the sound as unsettling and frustrating. For optimal stress reduction we need to feel a degree of control over the noise in our lives and be able to exercise the option to sit and think quietly or meditate. Parents, of course, have a more difficult time than most people in gaining this kind of environmental control. Earplugs are recommended prn for parents. Also, fantasy work on what life will be like after the children are in college may help. Earplugs actually are suggested if you sleep on a regular basis with a person who snores loudly.

One of the easier things to change in the environment is the color system we are exposed to at home and at work. You may have accommodated to that drab brown and green color in an institutional office, but adding an assortment of murals, posters, or inexpensive draperies can do wonders. Even more rewarding is paint and wallpaper. Do remember the influences of color in your clothing and even in the color of the car you drive. Changing the color systems in your environment can be a very helpful step toward creating a pleasant and relaxing place to spend your waking hours.

Now retrieve your list of physical environmental stressors and write what you will do about each item that is triggering distress. Look over your list of relaxing factors about your physical environment and see if there are ways to maximize your enjoyment of these.

Managing Your Social Environment

In discussing management of the social environment, we will be directing our thoughts toward ways of relating to others in order to prevent distress and promote tension-free, rewarding social living. We will discuss managing social stressors in international, national, community, and personal contexts. Since it is not very realistic to think in terms of changing others, we will focus on methods to manage the social stressors that involve possible changes in your own attitudes and behaviors as you interact with others. As you read this section and perhaps decide on some changes in your own social life, remember to make these changes slowly enough so that the changes themselves do not add significant distress to your life (refer to life change inventory, pages 74-75).

Taking on the world, of course, is a well-known source of distress. If international issues are a concern, however, you may want to consider joining an organization that supports world peace and health and education needs here and in other countries, in whatever organization seems to you to promote a less stressful world. There are many opportunities to take some action, albeit on a small scale, to help reduce international tensions and promote positive international social relationships. It may be helpful to think of any investment you make of your time, money, or energy as a maintenance fee toward preventing one of the most feared stressors—that of nuclear war.

On the national scene there are many things each of us can do to help manage social distress. One obvious way to influence the social environment in this country is to contribute to and become involved in political action. Support candidates who are responsive to your views. Support issues that contribute to more ease in our social environment. One such idea that may be worthy of promoting is the coverage by insurance companies of wellness education programs and biofeedback treatment so that people can be educated to prevent distress, be well, and be more in control of themselves and their lives. Certainly the basic structure of our social milieu would change if each person could actively demonstrate more control over his or her health and well-being since this would reduce the likelihood of feelings of threat and consequent aggressive and antisocial actions. Another issue of national social importance is the idea of our educational systems providing our children with thorough knowledge and practical experience in self-care, particularly in the areas of nutrition, exercise, and stress management in its most comprehensive sense. Yet another possible program would be better education for both children and adults in the detrimental effects of substance abuse, particularly drugs, alcohol, and cigarettes. Part of this program could be education in interpersonal relations so that our children would learn early in their lives how to initiate and maintain authentic, personal contact with one another without having to use substances to alter their experiences.

On a community level, perhaps the least stressful way to manage one's social environment is to be part of a community in which you share the predominant social mores. Also, taking deliberate steps to become acquainted with people in the neighborhood with the intent of building a strong support system is a stress-saving move and is probably most easily done in socially homogeneous neighborhoods. The Roseto story[10] illustrates this principle very well.

Roseto is an Italian-American community in east central Pennsylvania. It was founded in the late 1800s by a group of poverty-stricken Italian villagers who came to the United States, were shunned by others, and formed a strong, supportive social network in order to survive. Families worked very hard and looked after one another. Bruhn and Wolf began to study the social system of Roseto after the observation had been made that people of Roseto had a remarkably low death rate from myocardial infarction and a low incidence of mental illness, especially senile dementia, in comparison to people from two neighboring towns. The lack of disease was surprising because a large number of Rosetans were obese and the fact that incidences of smoking, hypertension, diabetes, measures of serum cholesterol concentration, and exercise habits were very similar in these three towns. Unlike its neighbors, however, Roseto had managed to hold on to its original social and ethnic values and customs in which family relationships were very close and families were mutually supportive. During the years the study was being conducted, some of the traditional values began to give way to more modern, Americanized ways of living. As these social changes began disrupting the Roseto social cohesion, the rate of fatal myocardial infarctions among the younger adults began to rise significantly.

Certainly the Roseto story is a clear example of the insulation value of a close-knit social system against distress. Because so many of us are living hundreds of miles from our families of origin and/or neighborhoods in which we were raised, it is up to us to create for ourselves the best possible substitute environment.

One way to improve our social environment is to seek out others of similar heritage and beliefs. Another is to develop a strong sense of identification with others that transcends cultural differences into a strong feeling and sense of "family." The more one expands his or her own boundaries of acceptance and identification with community members, the more that community will feel like a Roseto-type atmosphere.

Take just one or two minutes right now and let yourself fantasize your own neighborhood transformed into a tension-reducing, mutually-supportive place to live out your life. Perhaps you'll be able to imagine some small steps you could take to get this transformation started.

On a personal level of managing social stressors, there

are many possibilities for relating to others in helpful, nonstressful ways. One valuable way is belonging to a self-help group. This particular kind of social network is most helpful when some close friendships are formed, along with the sense of belonging to a larger group. Examples of well-known self-help groups are Alcoholics Anonymous, Al-Anon, Reevaluation Co-Counseling, Weight Watchers, Reach for Recovery, and Gamblers Anonymous. Analogous to the Roseto story, members of self-help groups are often brought into co-hesiveness from experiencing similar difficulties, sharing similar solutions, and being devoted to helping each other overcome these problems successfully. Many re-ligiously oriented groups offer their members a similar kind of social support system. Self-help groups need not be limited to recovery or religious themes. A group can be helpful when members are willing to share any of their life experiences and work together in a supportive way. Can you envision a group where you could share some significant issues and concerns in your life? Think about the types of people you would like to meet with, what you would like to discuss and how you would like to feel with others.

In my practice in Washington, D.C., I often see clients relate to their social environment by running for political office or getting a socially visible, politically appointed position. While they are admired for their philosophies or talents, politicians, entertainers, and sports figures may experience this relationship to their social system as a great buffer between themselves and distress. At some point, however, this admiration from others or the feeling that others are constantly wanting something from them begins to wear away this buffer and the need for a more intimate, day-by-day relation-ship arises. Some of the most severe stress reactions I have seen have been in clients who suddenly found themselves out of the limelight and back to being a "regular person." The effect of the loss of leadership or an admired position seems as catastrophic as with other clients who have suddenly lost their loved one through death or the breakup of an intimate relationship. In both instances, people are left with many serious questions about their personal and social identities. If you are often in a popular, publicly visible position, you would be wise to give solemn, quiet thought to what social role you could enjoy if the public role were suddenly to disappear.

Another way of being attached socially is having one or more intimate relationships. Brown and associates[11] conducted an interesting study about the relationship of social intimacy and depression in women. Their operational definitions of intimacy are as follows:

Score	*Definition*
A	Confides each day in someone with whom she has an emotionally intimate relationship.
B	Confides once a week in a friend, sister, or mother.
C	Confides less than once a week in anyone.
D	No confidant at all.

Protection from depression as a form of distress was found primarily in women who scored a high degree of intimacy. Those women who lacked an A score were found to suffer depression most consistently. Again, as in the Roseto story, long-lasting, consistent, intimate bonds, such as living in the same town as the rest of your family or celebrating a fiftieth wedding anniversary, are experiences that are becoming so rare as to be amazing. Marriage, the type of bonding that people used to be able to depend upon for security and safety from the distress of being alone, is not the center of adult life in our present culture. Even in the past fifteen years, attitudes toward marriage have changed radically in this country. I am seeing an increasing number of people in my practice who enter marriages or living-together arrangements with a strong feeling of commitment that does not, however, weather many storms. As adults in today's world, it seems that we must be able to make commitments and enjoy the fulfillment of these commitments, while at the same time realizing that changes can come about very quickly in ourselves and our partners and may lead to dissolution of the relationship. Being able to go somewhat gracefully through the steps of the grieving process over a relationship that has terminated seems to be one of the most important stress management talents to have these days. We will discuss this in detail in Chapter Five.

As we continue to identify methods of managing stressors from the social environment, you may want to have your list of ten relaxing and ten distressing elements of your social environment close by so that you can apply the principles directly to yourself.

Your awareness of the various characteristics of the social systems to which you belong and the roles you play in them has most likely been sharpened from doing the assessment earlier in this chapter. Awareness is the key to being able to conceptualize and deliberately use a method for managing any distress you may feel about being part of a social system. Let's say, for instance, you define your family system as an undifferentiated ego mass type of system. Once you realize this and note what distresses you about being a member of such a system, you are well on your way to thinking of methods for changing your own experience and perhaps the system itself. One method for handling the distress of feeling smothered by a system of this type is to keep your attention on your own experience and learn to verbalize these feelings to others in your family. Instead of believing the myth that "we" all think alike and behave alike, you can stay with your own awareness of what you are thinking and feeling and realize that you may indeed be different from other people in your family. At first, this recognition may become a stressor in itself, but differentiating yourself from others can be done gently over a period of time. If you see that your family fits the description of an undifferentiated ego mass, and you feel a great deal of distress from living in your family, you may want to seek some professional help from a family systems therapist who could assist you and your family in differentiating yourselves from one another and curtailing attempts to control one another.

As another example, suppose that you are part of a triangle in your family or your work system or other social system. If being in the triangle is distressing to you, a policy of no secrets may help loosen the boundaries of the triangle or dissolve them entirely. When all three people talk with each other freely and you avoid passing information from one person to the other, you can lessen this distress. Again, speaking for yourself and avoiding speaking for either of the other two people or blaming them for your feelings or position in the triangle are helpful methods of removing yourself from the triangle.

In my clinical practice I have seen people go to great lengths to maintain a sense of homeostasis in their social system, particularly in the family. One of the main tools people use to maintain homeostasis is reciprocity. You may have become aware that in some social systems you try to counterbalance someone else's behavior. For instance, someone may be very depressed or highly negative in their attitudes and you may find that you try to balance this by becoming overly jolly or a Pollyanna, or perhaps your spouse is not particularly motivated to do well in his or her career and so you become an overly high achiever in your career. People are often unaware that they are compensating for someone else's behavior, so it is important to be alert to this type of reaction. When you see that you are about to respond in a way designed simply to balance out someone else's thoughts or emotional state, stop and let yourself be aware of how you really feel and what you are really thinking. Express these thoughts and feelings instead. This action will give you more of a sense of your own integrity and less of a distressful sense of reacting to someone else's behavior. As you will remember from the section on assessment of the social environment, the concept of roles we play in social groups is a very important one. In considering roles in a generic sense, think of your own position in your family of origin. Were you, for instance, the oldest child, middle child, or youngest child, or, more specifically, the oldest brother of brothers, the oldest sister of brothers, or whatever? If so, see how you might still be automatically taking that role in present-day social systems. Roles, if automatically taken, often lead to distress since they are full of expectations of others' behavior and may be inappropriate for the situation. Suppose, for instance, that because you were an oldest child you still tend to automatically assume a leadership and caretaking role with others in a social group. You can begin now to evaluate this behavior rationally and try taking other roles such as letting others take care of you. Teaching yourself and learning from others how to be flexible in your role-taking within a group can be of great help in managing social environmental distress. Refer to *Family Constellation* by Walter Toman [12] for further information on the roles we play according to our original position in the family constellation.

You may be more aware at this point of what instrumental or task roles you typically take in a social system. Do you automatically take out the garbage or supervise others as they do the work? Or do you fulfill a sick role in the family? I spend a great deal of time in my practice helping people extricate themselves from constantly playing out the sick role in a family. I have often worked with women who have had migraine headaches for twelve to fourteen years. These women have usually effectively played out the whole family system's need for someone in the sick role. As the client (usually the mother in the family) utilizes biofeedback and psychotherapy to rid herself of the crippling headaches and thus of her sick role in the family, other members in the family will have accidents or become ill. In other words the system reacts as if a sick role of some sort must exist and if the role is not going to be filled by the usual person, other people will have to take their turns. This example of task role reciprocity is not unusual, but does illustrate how people unwittingly slip into roles that are highly distressful without knowing why. At times, even awareness that role switches can occur does not deter the family from playing this game.

If you realize that you are nearly always playing the same instrumental role in any of your social systems, you may want to try to identify some reasons for doing this and experiment with deliberately not taking this role in one or more of your social groups to see what happens. Remember that you may experience distress by changing roles, but try out the new behavior for a while and then assess whether this new effect is more or less distressing than the original.

When you assess the typical affective role that you play in your family or other social groups, perhaps you will be fortunate to find that you usually play a congruent role and feel free to say what you are thinking and feeling and do not use your role as a way to try to control others. This is the least distressful role to play. If you find that you occasionally get stuck in another affective role, such as the placater, blamer, computer, or distractor, focus your energy on becoming aware of when and with whom you play out one of these roles. Again, the best method for handling the distress that results from one of these four affective roles is to be aware of the role you are playing and experiment with playing another role instead.

Generally speaking, the more kinds of roles we can play effectively and the more freedom of choice we have within ourselves to play or not to play these roles, the lower our distress level will be. Also, we will experience more joy in our interpersonal relationships. In fact, being able to relate to one another with minimal role-playing leads to rewarding social experiences.

In our current culture we have more choices about how to relate to other people than any other culture in the history of civilization. This leaves us with the sometimes highly distressing task of trying to determine not only how to relate to others but which others to relate to most fully. In my practice I see many people who are in great distress from balancing time and energy between their work, home, and recreation. Washington is a city of workaholics where many people are predominantly devoted to their careers and yet wish to have satisfying intimate relationships at the same time. Because so many adults are single for periods of time in their lives nowadays, they contend with the distress of hovering on a boundary between feeling too alone or feeling too much pressure from others to relate to a social group. If this situation is similar to yours, you may get a perspective on your life by deciding whether you want to devote your time to building a social network or building your career, and by making some plans on how to divide your time later in your life. For instance, if you are a parent with small children, you may decide to expend most of your energy with your family, knowing that you can devote more energy to your career later. Again, use the principle of making deliberate decisions that are based on thoughts, feelings, and your sense of your own self and meaning of your life.

Another area of distress that must be managed well if we are to stay healthy concerns the expectations we have of others. We become upset when we experience incongruity between what we wanted from a social situation and what we actually got. Most likely, our expectations have come as a part of our socialization and may not match our actual experience of life. Do we still trust the group beliefs and expectations or do we depart from them and trust our own experience? For example, let's say you were raised to be honest and trust others to be honest also. Later a distressing conflict arises when you are robbed at gunpoint. Most people learn to settle these conflicts by becoming "realistically paranoid" about robberies (reflecting their personal experience) while maintaining trust in human nature generally (following values taught during socialization). Frequently we experience these information incongruities when we belong to social systems, especially if these systems promote certain beliefs and values that we experience as invalid in some way. From a stress management viewpoint, it is important to maintain awareness of your own experience to avoid the distress of feeling controlled by a group and its beliefs or pressured by such a group to the point of distress. Refer to Moss[13] for further theories of information incongruities and their relationship to stress.

Many of the principles we have covered that deal with our social environment as a source of stressors also apply to intimate relationships. Validating our expectations is very important when entering an intimate relationship in order to avoid distress and possible depression later. Becoming very clear as quickly as possible about the kinds of things you really want from the other person and what kinds of things you are willing to give to the other person is a significant first step toward a successful intimate relationship. Being aware of your own barriers to intimacy is also valuable. Realizing how your self-esteem is involved in this relationship is another important awareness. Watching for fears of intimacy and dealing with these forthrightly will prevent later distress. Keeping the relationship alive and exciting is one of the most difficult things people encounter in intimate relationships. An important factor in nurturing an intimate relationship is to adopt the orientation of wanting to talk about your feelings and thoughts openly even if this may seem like a high risk. Being able to expose your own fears and feelings of competition, jealousy, and irritation are important if done in an open, nonaccusatory manner. Being able to express appreciation, admiration, respect, and love in both sexual and nonsexual ways is certainly vital in keeping an intimate relationship alive and well. As mentioned before, maintaining many pleasurable, trusting, intimate relationships can be one of the very best hedges against distress and illness.

Now retrieve your list of social stressors which tend

to trigger either your "fight or flight" or "general adaptation syndrome" reflexes. Decide what action you would take to relieve each of these sources of distress. Then read your social support list and think of ways to enhance the effect of these factors in your life.

In this chapter you have had an opportunity to identify in some detail the physical and social environmental stressors in your life. While some of these stressors are unavoidable, most are of our own creation and under our control. We have noted that a thoughtful decision is necessary in evaluating the usefulness of changing a physical or social environmental situation. The typical error, however, is more toward omitting action to reduce distress than in taking action with futile results. In other words, more often than not we accommodate to stressful situations unnecessarily while our body/mind weakens under the stress. Perhaps part of the experience of finishing this chapter can be to adopt a firm resolve to efficiently and gracefully take action to modify your physical and social environment to reduce stress at every reasonable opportunity.

REFERENCES

1. Cassel, J. T. "Physical Illness in Response to Stress." *Social Stress*, ed. Sol Levine and Norman Scotch. Chicago: Aldine, 1970.

2. Fairbank, D. T., and Hough, R. L. "Life Event Classifications and the Event-Illness Relationship." *Journal of Human Stress*, September 1979, pp. 41-47.

3. Ross, C. E., and Mirowsky II, J. "A Comparison of Life-Event-Weighting Schemes: Change, Undersirability, and Effect-Proportional Indices." *Journal of Health and Social Behavior*, June 1979, *20*, 166-177.

4. Berrien, F. K. *General and Social Systems.* New Brunswick: Rutgers University Press, 1968.

5. Bowen, M. "The Use of Family Theory in Clinical Practice." *Changing Families,* ed. J. Haley. New York: Grune & Stratton, 1971.

6. Bowen, M. "The Use of Family Theory in Clinical Practice." *Changing Families,* ed. J. Haley. New York: Grune & Stratton, 1971.

7. Satir, V. *Peoplemaking.* Palo Alto: Science and Behavior Books, Inc., 1972.

8. Boyd, D. *Rolling Thunder.* New York: Random House, 1974.

9. Sierra Club, Environmental Action, P.O. Box 35027, Washington, DC 20013, and Solar Lobby, 1001 Connecticut Ave., NW, Suite 510, Washington, DC 20036.

10. Bruhn, J. G., and Wolff, S. *The Roseto Story.* Norman, OK: University of Oklahoma Press, 1979.

11. Brown, G. W., Bhrolchain, M. N., and Harris, T. "Social Class and Psychiatric Disturbance Among Women in an Urban Population." *Sociology,* 1975, *9,* 225-254.

12. Toman, W. *Family Constellation.* 2nd ed. New York: Springer Publishing Company, Inc., 1969.

13. Moss, G. E. *Illness, Immunity, and Social Interaction.* New York, John Wiley & Sons, 1973.

CHAPTER 4

Stress and the Body

Our bodies are wondrously organized collections of energy in visible form. They allow us movement, self-expression, and pleasure. They also present us with varying degrees of discomfort. Environmental, mental, emotional, and spiritual distress routinely make themselves known to us through bodily discomfort. In Chapter Two we explored the unity of mind and body and how the mind's stress translates into bodily discomfort, illness, and death. Conversely, the body is at times a source of mental and emotional distress. Viewing the body as one of our personal mediating factors (see conceptual model, page 15), we can see its potential as both a source of stressors and a source of support for reacting to and coping with stressors.

In this chapter, you will see that by handling bodily

distress effectively, you can prevent physical distress from becoming more intense or pervasive in the body and you can prevent physical distress from engendering mental, emotional, and spiritual distress. Since awareness is the primary step in any effective process of managing stress, we will first assess your body for signs of distress. Suggestions will then be given for taking command of your body and its ability to cope with stress. We will then discuss the relationship of nutrition and stress, active and passive forms of relaxation, and self-regulation of bodily signs of distress.

Assessing Your Body for Signs of Distress

Everyone's body carries signs of distress. Some of these signs are chronic and constant. Others are intermittent or relatively new. Being aware of the subtleties of your body's stress signals is fundamental to the process of managing stress well. To sharpen awareness of your body's distress, we will use several methods to analyze your general fitness and your specific stress responses.

General Body Awareness　　Be aware of your body at this moment. Notice your general comfort level. Which muscles are tighter than others? Do you have any aching or stiffness or spasms in your skeletal muscles? Is your stomach tense at all? How would you describe your breathing? Is it shallow and rapid? Do you pause for a while after you exhale? How would you evaluate your energy level?

Physical Reaction to Distress　　Now try an experiment to discover more about your body's usual stress reaction. Close your eyes and let yourself relive a stressful event (or make up one based on a fear of something stressful that could happen). Take your time to make this event as real as possible. When you feel yourself under stress, notice how your body feels. Is your pulse rate high? Are your hands cool and even a bit clammy? Is your stomach tight? Are you holding your breath? Is your jaw clenched? Are your shoulders and trapezius (the top of the shoulders and the back of the neck) tight?

Now let yourself relax and breathe deeply. Take a moment to write down a description of your body's reaction during the stressful moments you just experienced. Do you think your reaction was typical? What body parts do you remember tightening, holding, or speeding up in other stressful situations? Add these to your list so that you have the most complete profile possible of your own acute stress reaction. Refer to this list when we later discuss methods for managing bodily tension and distress.

Body Distress Inventory   For the rest of your body analysis, find a full-length mirror. Stand in front of the mirror, preferably without clothing, and observe your body closely. First, look for impressions of your general health status. Does your body look alive and vital in its energy level? Is your posture relaxed and balanced? Is your weight right for your bone structure and height? Is your weight well-distributed? What does the quality of your hair and teeth tell you about your general condition? Look at your skin closely. Do the tone and color indicate optimal circulation of blood? Answering these general questions can tell you something about your chronic level of distress as well as your condition for coping with new stressors today. Make a few notes now of your observations.

Now begin your observations to assess your body for specific signs of distress. First, reexamine your skin.

Notice any wrinkle lines in the face and neck area. Are these due to distress? Move your face into various positions to create these wrinkle tracks. Exaggerate these positions one at a time, noticing the feelings you experience in each position. Recall the situations in which you made these faces. Were these stressful situations? Notice moments in the future when you make these same stressful facial expressions. By becoming aware of these occasions, you will have the option of continuing to make the same expression or choosing another way to handle the distress.

Another important quality to observe about your skin is its temperature. You will recall that during distress it is common for the blood to shift away from peripheral areas of the body, such as the hands and feet. Circulation to these areas can become chronically impaired if your circulatory system has been directly affected by stressors. Here is a simple way to check yourself. Place the backs of the last two joints of your fingers against the front of your neck to see if your fingers feel cool by comparison. A more precise way to monitor this is to use a thermometer against the pad of an index finger to get a temperature reading. Skin temperature of the hands should be at least 85° F. A reading of 90–95° F indicates better circulation and probably a more relaxed body generally. There are ways to keep your hands warm and thereby elicit a generalized relaxation response which we will discuss later in the section on biofeedback.

Yet another characteristic to notice about the skin is the areas of perspiration. If you are not perspiring now, let yourself recall where and how much you perspire. Do you perspire heavily under stress? Sometimes, perspiration is a person's first clue that he or she is under stress.

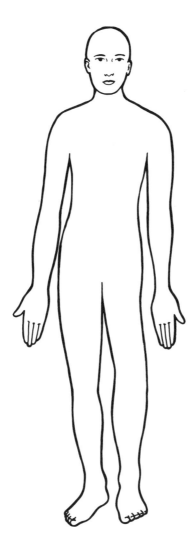

Figure 13: Using the above outline you can complete your body distress analysis.

Next, notice your posture in the mirror. Is your head balanced over your spine or have you bent it over or shoved it back? Do you stand with your knees locked or are you more flexible? Notice which direction the backs of your hands face. They should face forward. If they do not, notice what your arm position is doing to your shoulders, chest, back, and breathing. You may need to exaggerate your position to make it more obvious. Is any strain you find related to the way you try to handle stress? Do you notice a difference between your left and right sides? Is one hip higher than the other? Sometimes people let their trapezius muscle become chronically tense so that it contracts upward. I call this condition "shoulder earmuffs." Do you have this symptom? If so, see if you can associate this condition with any particular stressor. (Usually this type of tenseness is a general reaction to many different stressors.) See if you can rotate your shoulders in circles while breathing slowly and deeply, and let go of some of that tension. Continue to notice any other imbalances in your posture. Exaggerate these positions so you can gain full awareness of any stressful feelings or pain that accompany these aberrations.

Now test your flexibility. When people are tense from distress, they lose some degree of flexibility. Slowly walk around, bend, twist, and turn. Do you notice any blocks to full mobility of the head and neck, arms, legs, or spine? Take time to clearly note these areas and give some thought to the reasons certain movements are inhibited. Which muscles are stiff? Press on these muscles with your fingers and thumbs to get a full sense of the character of these tight muscles. What stressful feelings may be locked inside them? Are any muscles so tight that they tremble? See if you can breathe and move in ways that will relax them. Remember that muscle tension is a primary reaction to stressors and that we tend to become accustomed to increasingly higher tension levels without noticing the discomfort that accompanies tension. Chronically tense muscles also rob us of energy. Furthermore, they lead us to feel, at least on an unconscious level, that we are more vulnerable to distress since we cannot deal with stressors from a physically fit and flexible stance when we are tense.

Stand or sit still now and observe your pulse and respiratory rates. Since heart rates can vary with body rhythm throughout the day by 20 to 30 beats per minute[1], it is difficult to establish an exact pulse rate for everyone. (Usually a range of 75–80 beats per minute is normal.) You may want to keep a record of your pulse and respiratory rate for a few days under various conditions to collect information on your normal rates when at rest or under stress.

Other ways we create bodily distress are to unknowingly clamp down on a part or section of our bodies or to protect some area. See if you are in one of these patterns. Get comfortable and close your eyes. Touch your entire body in a systematic manner. As you do, be sensitive to your thoughts and emotions about each area of your body. Are there vulnerable areas that you try to protect from stress? Are there areas you try to hide? Are there areas you dislike? How do you create tension as you react to these perceptions about your body? You may want to make a few more notes right now about areas of distress and reasons for distress in your body.

Using the drawing on page 109, take a red pen and note, in your own code, what kind of distress you are aware of experiencing with any regularity in your body. Use the data you just collected plus any memories of other distress signs. When this information is recorded, take a blue or green pen and make note of bodily areas and functions that are relaxed and in fine form. Take time to study your body drawing so that you heighten your awareness of both the problem areas and the strong, well areas. Can you let yourself discover more about the reasons why certain parts of your body are more prone to be stress-reactive than others? What stressors are most clearly related to which physical reactions? Which of your thoughts trigger an unpleasant physical reaction? What thoughts calm your body?

The last task in your body distress inventory is a general assessment. Lie down in a comfortable position and let your body relax. As you do, assess your body for those areas that relax easily. Which areas are tense? What can you do to encourage the tense parts to relax? Add this information to your notes.

Biorhythms and Distress   Our bodies have internal clocks that control the cycles of many biological functions. These body rhythms are the subject of interest to scientists from a relatively new discipline called chronobiology. Chronobiologists have discovered that each gland and organ has its own rhythm of activity and that they behave in a synchronous manner so that even though the lengths of rhythmic cycles change, the pattern is predictable. Hilts[2] reports that heart rate, blood pressure, body temperature, alertness, eye-hand coordination, energy level, cell division rate, mood, memory, and more than 36 body chemical levels vary according to their own rhythms in our bodies each day. These variations are called circadian fluctuations (see Figure 14).

Synchronization of these natural internal rhythms can be disturbed by stressors such as shift work, flying across several time zones, and erratic habits of waking and sleeping. Once the numerous rhythms are out of phase with one another, more stress is felt in the form

CIRCADIAN/INFRADIAN CYCLES

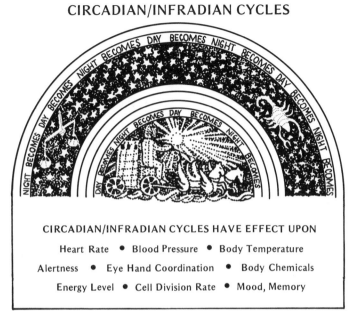

CIRCADIAN/INFRADIAN CYCLES HAVE EFFECT UPON

Heart Rate • Blood Pressure • Body Temperature

Alertness • Eye Hand Coordination • Body Chemicals

Energy Level • Cell Division Rate • Mood, Memory

Figure 14: Circadian fluctuations are cycles of biological functions regulated by internal clocks.

of irritability, exhaustion, and more than usual susceptibility to illness. Interacting with others during this psychophysiological state can cause yet another wave of distress!

Being aware of your own body rhythms allows you to acknowledge your usual ups and downs, predict these periods, and accommodate to them. Living with your rhythms rather than desynchronizing them offers a much more pleasant and unstressed lifestyle. Awareness of your own rhythms can be in terms of a circadian (approximately 24-hour) cycle and an infradian (days, weeks, or longer) time frame. Knowing about both of these types of rhythms is important when making plans to avoid or minimize stress. Most of us are aware of

114

CHART FOR HOURLY BIORHYTHM RECORD

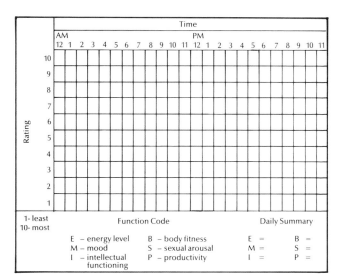

Figure 15: Total your rating for each Function Code and divide by the number of hours that are recorded to identify your Daily Summary Score.

being "night" or "day" people; for example, some prefer to stay up for late night activities, while others prefer to rise early in the morning, feeling most energetic then. Knowing only this about your own rhythms can influence your choice of job and living arrangements.

How can you calculate your body rhythms? Today there are many kits and computers on the market supposedly able to calculate your rhythms for you; however, according to Luce[3] each person's rhythms are unique within ranges of possibilities. Using materials that predict a person's rhythms based on birth dates and standard curves could give erroneous predictions, which could then become self-fulfilling prophecies.

For purposes of accuracy, then, one's own special cyclic variations should be discovered. Luce warns us,

CHART FOR DAILY BIORHYTHM RECORD

	August																							
	1	2	3	4	5	6	7	8	9	10	11	12	13	14	15	16	17	18	19	20	21	22	23	24
10																								
9																								
8																								
7																								
6																								
5																								
4																								
3																								
2																								
1																								

Rating

1- least
10- most

Figure 16: Record your Daily Summary Score to chart rhythms on a monthly basis.

however, that "biological rhythms have sometimes appeared to resemble the smile of a Cheshire cat—faint, taunting, appearing, and disappearing" and that changes may be difficult to perceive from the raw data we gather about ourselves. Nevertheless, you may wish to try to chart some of your rhythms so that you can lighten expectations of yourself at times when you may not be functioning at peak level and schedule important events when you are in top form and least likely to be stressed.

Look at Figure 15. By placing a code letter opposite a scale of one to ten, you can rate an aspect of yourself for a particular hour. You can chart different or additional rhythmic functions by assigning a code letter to each function. When you have done this for several days, color code the functions by connecting all the Es with one color, all the Ms with another, and so forth, until you see some patterns emerging.

You can also chart these rhythms on a monthly basis by recording your Daily Summary Score for each function on the Daily Record of Biorhythms (see Figure 16). Follow the same procedure for color coding mentioned above to see what patterns begin to emerge. Definite patterns can be traced, then, into future hours, days, and months, so that stressful events will not be loaded into the time frames that appear vulnerable.

Body Stress Record Related to the exercise of recording your biorhythms is another exercise in which you keep a record of bodily tension. Not only will patterns of tension emerge over days and weeks, but the process of recording increases awareness and thus allows an opportunity to relieve tension. Once awareness of tension becomes habitual, you may find yourself developing an automatic relaxation response to your first signs of tension.

Charting bodily distress can be done using the same format as in Figure 15. In this exercise you write hourly a code indicating the body part and its stress beside the appropriate number. For instance, a moderate stomach ache at 7 A.M. could be coded as SA opposite the number six. Again, this record is valuable mainly because of the awareness to be gained, but useful patterns may emerge. You may want to see how the bodily tension data compare with the biorhythm data.

Managing Bodily Distress

To manage bodily distress, we will first consider bodily nourishment—how to manage food intake to avoid distressing the body and how to eat during stressful times.

Next we will look at active and passive forms of physical relaxation, ranging from aerobic exercising to biofeedback and meditation to counteract the physical tension associated with the stress response. Finally, we will consider ways to handle specific bodily distress states such as being overweight, in pain, or having a serious disease such as cancer.

Three problems arise when we consider ways of managing bodily distress. One is the dilemma of how to release tension, either old, pent-up tension from as far back as childhood or as recent as last week's argument with the budget director. Usually, exercise, massage, and emotional expression of suppressed feelings are useful in releasing this stored tension. Another problem is how to let go of bodily distress as it is building. This takes acute awareness of the buildup process and knowledge of how to exercise, relax, and express feelings to dissipate the tension thoroughly. The final problem is how to keep the body free most of the time of damaging tension so it can withstand stressors and regain homeostasis quickly with no damage. Keeping the body relaxed means for most people a repertoire of several methods which an individual can use appropriately in a variety of situations.

Nutrition and Bodily Distress   What we take into our bodies can initiate a stress response directly, create fatigue and irritability, or simply fail to support the body's attempt to regain homeostasis after a stress response. Eating knowledgeably can help you avoid both short-term distress such as indigestion and wide fluctuations in blood sugar as well as the long-term distress of such dietary-influenced problems as heart disease and diabetes.

Unfortunately, the field of nutrition is filled with contradictory experimental results and clinical opinion.

Witness the opposing viewpoints of the well-known diet experts Robert Atkins and Nathan Pritikin, who contend that each other's diets can cause serious problems. Another controversy is the disagreement between traditionalists who say we do not need to take vitamins and the dissenters who claim that we do need vitamin supplements because in these modern times our bodies are stressed and not nourished well by food that is too thoroughly processed after being produced in depleted soil.

Since each of us has a unique biochemical makeup and metabolic process, one diet for stressful periods would not suffice for everyone. You may want to seek individual assessment of your nutritional needs to be sure you are as well nourished as possible. Some nutritionists you consult might suggest blood work and/or hair analysis as part of the evaluation. Dietary suggestions can then be tailored to your vitamin and mineral needs and your activity and eating habits.

Many of us will head for our favorite foods when highly distressed. These may be comforting psychologically but, at the same time, may add to the stress the body is already enduring. An example of this is to eat a large amount of chocolate and sugar to find comfort.

During periods of distress, consideration of both quality and quantity of food is important. As Brintzenhofe[4] suggests, moderation is an important principle to follow during times of high stress. Adhering to this principle can help lessen distress on the digestive and metabolic functions of the body. Moderation of quantity is obviously important, since too much food at one sitting can cause pain as well as stress on the body as it tries to handle too much protein, fat, and carbohydrate. When food is eaten in too great a quantity, the body may not be able to break it down into simpler substances for absorption and it may be transported to the intestine in undigested form. If kept in the intestine a long time, these whole foods may be acted upon by bacteria rather than enzymes and may produce substances which are toxic to the body. Another effect of overload can be drowsiness, which can cause distress if you are trying to go back to work on a project that must be done quickly or must go to an important meeting shortly after eating too much.

Besides quantity, quality of the food itself and quality in the experience of eating are also important considerations in nutritional management of distress. Relaxing during a meal and thoroughly enjoying the flavors and textures of your food is a healthy contrast to eating "on the run." Chewing your food well, eating with friends, sharing laughter rather than stomach-churning topics, and listening to music add quality and reduce tension.

If your work situation allows you little time to eat, you may find fresh juices enjoyable and easy to digest. A juice extractor used on fruits and vegetables separates the liquid (which contains an abundance of vitamins and minerals) from the fiber. Drinking this juice saves the body work; yet the nutrients can be absorbed in minutes. An additional benefit is that the chemicals used on fruits and vegetables remain in the fiber so that another source of distress is avoided.

Eating fresh "live energy" foods whenever possible helps your body get a high ratio of nutritional value for the energy expended in digesting the food. Allowing food to travel quickly enough through your digestive system is important, too. Eating plenty of fiber foods such as fruits, bran, leafy vegetables, and brown rice can aid the movement of food byproducts so that the stress of constipation and inflammatory diseases of the colon can be avoided or diminished.

Water also aids in digestion and elimination of waste and toxic substances from the body. Adequate water intake is essential in maintaining a homeostatic state and life itself. Optimal intake varies according to such factors as your body weight, metabolic rate, the temperature and humidity of your environment, and the amount of exercise you do along with your dietary habits.

Stressful periods tend to deplete some nutrients from our bodies, particularly vitamin C and several of the B vitamins. Vitamin C (ascorbic acid) deficiency leads to scurvy or anemia and increases susceptibility to infection. Ballentine[5] asserts that loss of vitamin C and catecholamines into the urine is higher in people who react to events with anxiety than in those who are tranquil. The amount of vitamin C required during stressful periods varies among individuals and with the level of anxiety manifested psychophysiologically. Vitamin C is found in high quantity in citrus fruits, leafy green vegetables, and tomatoes.

A depletion of B complex vitamins can result from stressful experiences and, if serious, can create more distress in the form of such problems as anxiety, depression, insomnia, anemia, and weakness. B vitamins are found together in nature and are best taken together, although some B vitamins are more stress-related than others. Supplementing your diet with one could cause an imbalance or depletion of another. Ballentine[6] suggests the germ and bran of seeds such as nuts, beans, and peas as rich sources of vitamin B complex. He warns that although yeast can be a fine source of vitamin B complex, high uric acid levels may result in individuals who take more than two or three tablespoons a day.

Other nutrients of value during stressful periods are calcium, potassium, and magnesium, all of which are related to neuromuscular functioning. Again, the amounts needed are unique to each person and a hair analysis test can provide information about your own levels of minerals and possible needs for supplements.

Another concern is the ingestion of foods that contain harmful substances. These substances may be additives, allergenic agents, or simply too much salt, sugar, and caffeine.

Foreign substances in the form of additives to our foods can be stressful to our bodies. Ingesting foods that have been sprayed, processed, or preserved with chemicals is easy to do; however, not all chemicals are equally harmful. If you wish to learn more about additives, refer to *Your Health Under Seige*[7] which lists ingredients in foods and their possible physiological effect. Chemicals used to color, preserve, or flavor foods can place a stress on the liver, the organ involved in breaking down these substances. Following the old rule, "if it won't rot, don't eat it," may help you avoid highly-processed foods. Brintzenhofe[8] suggests peeling whole fruits and vegetables or washing them with a solution of one tablespoon vinegar to two quarts water as a way to neutralize sprays that may have been used in growing them.

Allergens can cause a wide range of distress in our bodies. Headaches, respiratory problems, gastrointestinal upsets, dermatologic problems, and mental/emotional variances can be triggered by allergens in food. You may be familiar with any major food allergies you have; however, you may be interested in discovering the more subtle ones that cause distress as well. Mandell's popular book, *5-Day Allergy Relief System*,[9] may give you some useful information.

Most of us know from clinical experience the stressful results of too much salt, which causes water retention and creates such symptoms as irritability and high blood pressure. Too much sugar can also cause a high degree of distress. We may take in sugar to give us a boost in energy, but it may cause a reactive hypoglycemia with corresponding symptoms of headache, dizziness, fatigue, and irritability. In this state of depressed mood and decreased alertness, we are prone to make distressing errors. Another disadvantage of refined sugar is that it must utilize B complex vitamins from the body to supply energy. It is possible, then, to experience B vitamin depletion as well. Eating small, well-balanced meals that do not contain refined sugars is one way to prevent a significant amount of distress each day.

Caffeine is another common trigger of bodily distress. Caffeine is found in tea, coffee, chocolate, and many cola beverages and acts as a powerful stimulant, giving the sense of being "up" and having high energy. It may also, however, cause irritability and sleeplessness. Concentration may actually be disrupted. People who have stopped drinking caffeine often comment on what a relief it is to be operating on their own natural energy rather than experiencing the ups and downs of caffeine use.

If you have decided to change to a lower stress diet, do it gradually. Remember, change itself is stressful. Exchanging coffee, sweet rolls, and chocolates for fruits, vegetables, and tofu too suddenly can be hazardous to your stress level!

Active Relaxation to Manage Bodily Distress   Both active and passive forms of exercise can initiate a general relaxation response that counters the stress response and allows the body to return to a prestressed state. Active exercises, such as jogging, tennis, and walking, can improve circulation and stretch muscles to relieve tension. For some people, active exercise has a relaxing psychological effect as well. Large muscle exercise after a work shift may be one of the best ways to relax the tension accumulated during these hours.

The only major drawback to careful use of active or passive exercise to manage bodily distress is that exercise may serve as a temporary relief to the physical manifestation of a psychological or spiritual problem. For instance, let's say you get in the habit of jogging to relieve tension and find it works beautifully. Let's also say you have a daily conflictual relationship with your spouse or a co-worker and use jogging to relieve your tension rather than working on the relationship. If the conflict increases, you may have to jog more and more in order to get the same relief. There are people who become addicted to this way of handling stress rather than confronting and resolving the underlying conflicts. Although this pattern may not be common as a neurotic style, being aware of your reasons for exercising is important.

Active relaxation through exercise helps manage stress by relieving tension directly and quickly and helps build physical fitness as a general aid in handling stressors. Vigorous kinds of exercising can promote the relaxation response and help rid the body of by-products of the fight or flight response while the body returns to a homeostatic state. Exercising is particularly relaxing if there are no elements of competition present in your experience. Being nonjudgmental of your own performance helps too. Exercising can be a transcendent experience, allowing you to rise above cares and worries of the day. This type of experience has been reported often by clients who practice a relaxation tape before or after running or walking. Active relaxation can help prevent stress reactions by enhancing a feeling of being alive, alert, and flexible.

Other more general reasons for exercise as a technique in managing bodily distress are that it heightens your energy level, makes circulation more efficient so that recovery from stressful episodes and illness is quicker, increases endurance so that enough oxygen and nutrients are available to the body cells and wastes are eliminated easily, strengthens the body and improves posture, and helps control weight. Active relaxation can also make a positive impact on mood, self-confidence, sexual energy level, and the ability to sleep restfully.

Is your present weekly exercise enough and of a quality that helps you relieve tension? If you are a staff nurse, you may feel you get plenty of exercise moving at a near gallop all day or night, but does that kind of motion relieve tension or build it?

Ask yourself now if you are satisfied with your fitness level. Do you look as if you are in shape? Can you relax your muscles easily? Are you as strong as you want to be? Is your coordination good? Is your body flexible enough? Can you endure long walks or going up two flights of steps, or do you get easily fatigued? Are you satisfied with the condition of your respiratory, cardiovascular, digestive, and neuromuscular systems? Do you feel alive and on the move?

To test yourself on physical fitness, try the exercises in Figure 17. The results may help you decide whether or not to devote yourself to a program of exercise.

The phrase "program of exercise" may evoke immediate revulsion or panic. Have you already gone on a similar program 22 times? If your life is sedentary, it may be particularly difficult to consider aerobic dancing, swimming, tennis, or jogging. Sometimes it is helpful to only slightly modify your lifestyle (by taking a short walk during your lunch break) and gradually working up to an active exercise program (by walking to work).

A SIMPLE FITNESS TEST

Flexibility

With legs spread to shoulder width, reach back and touch behind the knees.

Power

While someone holds your hands for balance, jump up from a kneeling position.

Strength

In a push-up position with back straight, bend elbows and touch forehead to one hand, then the other.

Balance

With eyes closed, balance on right leg—if right-handed—left leg—if left-handed—for 20 seconds.

Figure 17: A simple fitness test for a male age 50-60 or a female age 40-50. (Adapted with permission from Macmillan Publishing Company, Inc. See original for complete range of exercises for various age groups.)

Another suggestion is to stay in bed five minutes longer and do some simple stretching exercises. This routine can be a relaxing and energizing way to start the day, yet it requires very little effort. See Figure 17 for sample exercises or make up your own according to which muscles seem to need stretching on any given morning. Watching a cat wake up from a nap may provide inspiration and instruction for this endeavor.

All day there are many opportunities to practice stretching exercises. They can be done while waiting in bank and grocery lines, while talking on the telephone, and even while stopping at a red light when driving. Anderson's book *Stretching* [10] is an excellent guide for learning this art. Another way to integrate tension release exercises into the day is to exaggerate your motions as you dress, fix meals, and work. Walking up steps rather than using an elevator is useful. Running in place for a minute or two while thinking is another possibility. Isometric types of exercising can be fit into your schedule without much disruption, too, though they are not as relaxing as stretching exercises.

The change from a sedentary life to an active one must be made gradually or the change itself will produce stress. The same principle applies to the transition from being still to engaging in vigorous exercise like running or playing tennis. Warm-up stretching movements for five to ten minutes help reduce the chances of injury or strain in preparing to exert your body. A similar five-to-ten minute cool-down period after exercise assists you in returning gradually to a quieter state.

For exercise to be a tension-releasing experience, competition should be eliminated. Let others talk about running ten miles a day without feeling you must match that story at the next get-together. Also be aware of the temptation to achieve and push too hard simply from

STRETCHING EXERCISES

Stretching is easy to learn, but there is a right way and a wrong way to stretch. The right way is a relaxed, sustained stretch with your attention focused on the muscles being stretched. The wrong way (unfortunately practiced by many people), is to bounce up and down, or to stretch to the point of pain: these methods can actually do more harm than good.

Start the day with some relaxed stretches so your body can function more naturally. Tight and stiff muscles will feel good from comfortable stretching. It may be helpful to take a hot shower to get warm before you stretch.

Pull your right knee to your chest. For this stretch keep the back of your head on the floor or mat if possible, but don't strain. Hold an easy stretch for 30 seconds. Repeat, pulling your right leg toward your chest. Be sure to keep your lower back flat. This is a very good position for the legs, feet, and back.

Interlace your fingers behind your head at about ear level. Now, use the power of your arms to slowly pull your head forward until you feel a slight stretch in the back of the neck. Hold for 5-10 seconds, then slowly return to the original starting position. Do this 3-4 times to gradually loosen the upper spine and neck.

Figure 18: Suggestions for stretching exercises. (Adapted with permission from Shelter Publications.)

internal pressure. Make yourself aware of any progress, encourage yourself, and reward yourself in some manner after exercising. Regularity of practice is important in order to feel a sense of progress.

Figure 19 shows a list of many activities with corresponding beneficial effects. One of the most important criteria for choosing an activity is that you enjoy it, not just that you see it on a chart and decide it would be good for you. A physician specializing in sports medicine or a health professional from the field of holistic health may be able to assist you in choosing an exercise. Also, of course, are the alternatives of joining a fitness center and receiving guidance on an exercise program tailored to your needs. You may also find Kuntzleman's book *Rating the Exercises*[11] useful in helping you decide which exercises are best for you.

Passive Relaxation to Manage Bodily Distress   There are many passive methods of relaxation that counteract the effects of stress. Most of these methods focus on the relaxation of muscles since muscle tension is clearly high during a stress response, is often partially retained, and gradually builds up over the years. Accommodation to great degrees of muscle tension is possible. I often see new clients whose muscles feel like bands of steel, and they report no pain. As relaxation therapy begins, however, they become aware of the tension and pain that have been present for years. The more they learn to experience a relaxed, tension-free state, the more they can be aware of tension and let it go. Physiologically speaking, this action sends new messages to the reticular activating system, which responds by allowing neuromuscular quieting to occur. Our inner experience of this quieting is to feel pleasantly relaxed in a whole mind/body/spirit sense and, if it is needed, to feel sleepy and

SPORTS CHART

Activity	Heart	Muscle endurance	Muscle power	Coordination	Balance	Flexibility
Aerobic dancing	●	●	●	●	●	●
Bicycle riding	●	●	●		●	
Bowling				●		
Canoeing (bow)	●	●			●	
Canoeing (stern)	●	●	●	●	●	
Golf (walking)	●	●		●		
Handball	●	●	●	●	●	●
Hiking	●	●	●		●	
Horseback riding			●		●	
Jogging	●	●			●	
Long brisk walk	●	●				
Mountain climbing	●	●	●	●	●	
Sailing	●		●	●		
Short walk	●					
Softball		●		●		
Swimming	●	●	●	●		●
Table tennis	●			●		
Tennis	●	●	●	●	●	●
Walk-run-walk	●	●			●	

Figure 19: Physical benefits of various sports. (Adapted with permission from California Raisin Advisory Board.)

go on to enjoy restful sleep.

In this section we will look at various passive relaxation methods such as biofeedback, progressive relaxation, autogenics, imagery, meditation, yoga, bioenergetics, Feldenkrais work, Tai Chi, and hands-on therapies, such as massage, acupressure, reflexology, polarity, and therapeutic touch. Any of these methods, like active relaxation activities, must be practiced in a regular disciplined manner if noticeable results are desired. Let's begin with biofeedback.

Biofeedback　　Biofeedback uses various types of instruments to monitor psychophysiologic functions that may or may not be within a person's awareness. Information about biological conditions, such as skin surface temperature, muscle tension, galvanic skin response (skin perspiration), brain wave activity, blood pressure, and heart rate, can be obtained. This information is transformed by instruments into audio and visual signals. These signals report changes in the system being monitored so that the person is able to "see" and "hear" what is going on in his or her body. Hence the term biofeedback. A common example of feedback is a signal that increases in pitch each time the temperature of the skin surface of a finger rises one-tenth of a degree and decreases as skin temperature lowers. Sometimes a visual readout of the temperature is also provided. Receiving this information allows the person to know about changes in the dilation and constriction of the vessels in the monitored hand. You will recall that during a stress response peripheral vessels contract causing cooling of the skin on the hands and feet. Using a biofeedback instrument as an aid to learn to warm the hands can help create a general relaxation response. We will see in more detail how people learn to warm their hands when we discuss pain management later in this chapter.

Biofeedback instruments can help people with specific relaxation needs to gain voluntary control over their bodies and reduce or relieve entirely such problems as tension and migraine headaches, neck and back pain, hypertension, asthma, stuttering, insomnia, epilepsy, bruxism, temporomandibular joint syndome, and Reynaud's disease. Biofeedback instruments are also used to help people with specific anxieties and phobias. No matter what the specific complaint may be, in the initial sessions clients are usually taught general relaxation methods.

Often I receive calls from people who want to learn general relaxation methods by using biofeedback instruments. If they elect individual sessions, I first do a biofeedback evaluation, monitoring several body systems under neutral, stressful, and relaxed conditions to see how their bodies react to these situations.

Let's say from a biofeedback evaluation of Judy I discover that she has outstandingly high muscle tension even when at rest. We would then investigate to see which muscle groups are most tense and start with a muscle group she could learn to relax most easily (perhaps her forearm muscles). As Judy watches and listens to the electromyograph (EMG), which is a sensitive indicator of muscle contractions, she gains information about the fluctuations in her muscle tension. She then tries various ways of relaxing her muscles until she finds methods that, according to the EMG feedback, reduce her tension level. Finding the methods that are effective gives Judy a new sense of control over the discomfort and fatigue she was experiencing due to her chronic muscle tension. Judy can practice these successful methods at home, and her progress can be monitored weekly until she is able to deeply relax many muscle groups at will. She will then be able to practice relaxing deeply during various stressful life situations.

Many of the following deep muscle relaxation methods are used in conjunction with biofeedback therapy. They will be presented in enough detail to enable you to practice them at home. You may want to consider arranging a biofeedback evaluation session for yourself so that you have an accurate record of your tension levels at the beginning of your relaxation training. Later you may wish to arrange another evaluation session to get data on your progress and an opinion about whether specific biofeedback work would be beneficial.

Progressive Relaxation   In 1929 Dr. Edmund Jacobson wrote a book called *Progressive Relaxation*, which was a technical book on neuromuscular relaxation. Jacobson, in a later book, wrote that "to be relaxed is a direct physiological opposite of being excited or disturbed."[12] He devoted much of his professional life to developing what he called progressive relaxation methods to reduce tension and conserve energy. Dr. Jacobson intended this method to be used in place of tranquilizing agents.

The progressive relaxation method is a process of becoming aware of various muscles and muscle groups, tensing these deliberately, then allowing them to deeply relax. The sequence is "progressive" because each step increases the depth of relaxation and moves from one group to another in an orderly way.

Jacobson's original exercises are too lengthy to present in entirety, so I will give some examples that you can use and apply to other muscle groups in your body if you wish. These are helpful if you wish to be somewhat physically active while relaxing or are frustrated, angry, or agitated. If none of these conditions applies to you, this method may seem like too much work and

you may want to skip the tensing part and just relax the
various muscle groups. Following are some suggestions
in a drastically shortened form of Jacobson's exercises:

Choose a quiet place where you will not be
interrupted. Sit or lie down so that you are comfortable and can breathe easily. Breathe deeply
and exhale slowly, letting out tension from your
body in a general way.

Now make your hands into fists and squeeze
them very hard, tightening your arm muscles at
the same time. Hold the tension as long as you can
and notice the subtle details of the experience
of this tension. Then let go of the tension entirely
and exhale fully. Notice then the contrast of the
relaxed state and tense state. When you are
ready, repeat this process.

Next, point your toes toward your head and
tighten all the muscles you can in your feet
and legs. Hold the tension as long as possible
and notice all the various types of tension in your
feet and legs. Then let go of the tension as thoroughly as you can as you exhale fully. Again notice
the contrast between the tense state and the relaxed state. When you feel like it, do this again.

Now tighten the muscles in your buttocks and
hold these muscles tense as long as you can, carefully noticing the sensations of tension. As you
exhale and relax fully, let the sensations of relaxation deepen in your legs and feet. When ready,
repeat this step.

Now tighten the muscles in your abdomen by
pulling your abdomen inward toward your back.
Hold the tension and be fully aware of it. Then
exhale completely as you let go and let the relax-

ation spread to your buttocks and legs. Repeat when you are ready.

Next tighten your shoulders and back carefully—just enough to feel tension clearly. Hold it for a few seconds, then exhale and relax, noticing the contrast and letting your whole body relax more. Repeat this when you are ready.

Now tense every muscle in your face by closing your eyes tightly, frowning, pursing your lips, clenching your jaw, and tightening your other facial and neck muscles. Observe the tension closely and then exhale and relax, letting yourself enjoy the contrast and relief. Repeat when ready.

Last, tense your entire body by tightening all the muscles as just directed. Hold these muscles tight, experience the tension fully, and exhale and relax completely, letting tension go and relaxation sensations spread throughout your entire body. Repeat if you wish.

If you are serious about learning this method, practicing twice a day is necessary. You may find that you concentrate on some muscle groups more than others. If a muscle group is particularly tense, you may find that tightening and relaxing this area throughout the day is helpful. Remember that proper breathing is important with this method.

Autogenics   While Jacobson was developing progressive relaxation, Dr. Johannes Schultz was deriving autogenic training from hypnosis as a method of self-induced deep relaxation. This method involves concentration on certain phrases to set a mood, relax muscles, and increase blood flow. Autogenic training can be described as concentrative relaxation. It is important that passive concentration be maintained. A concept of achievement or any attempt to accomplish something specific will trigger your sympathetic nervous system. Since this is an altered state of consciousness procedure, it should not be done by someone with a tendency to hallucinate or experience troublesome altered states. The basic phrases are as follows:

> I am at peace.
> My right arm (or left, if left-handed) is very heavy.
>   (Then opposite arm.)
> My right (or left) hand is warm.
>   (Then opposite hand.)
> My pulse is calm and strong.
> My breath is calm and regular.
> My solar plexus is glowing warm.
> My forehead is pleasantly cool.[13]

As with other relaxation exercises, be sure you are in a quiet, comfortable place and will not be interrupted. If you are hungry, have a snack but do not eat a large meal. Sit or lie comfortably so that you can breathe easily. Close your eyes and take a deep, relaxing breath, letting the cares of the day leave your mind. Begin with the mood phrase, "I am at peace." Concentrate on this thought, repeating it mentally very slowly about four times. To return to an alert state of consciousness, move your arms, take a deep breath, exhale, and open your eyes when you are ready. This may be all you will do for the first week, practicing twice each day. Slowly add one phrase after another to the mood phrase in your practice sessions. Continue to practice two times a day until you feel you have mastered autogenic training. Individual experiences will vary widely in the effects of the phrases. As the weeks go by, your body will probably respond more quickly to the phrases. If you enjoy the format, you may wish to think of your own positive phrases and affirmations to use in calming and balancing your body.

Relaxation Tapes I have already mentioned my "Basic 101" relaxation tape, which I give to nearly every client and use in conjunction with biofeedback as a way to learn the relaxation response. There are many relaxation tapes on the market, and they vary in quality. The advantage of using a tape is that you can experience a more complete, passive "letting go" than with self instructions because you only take in information rather than expend effort to give information to yourself. For this reason you may even want to record some of the relaxation exercises presented in this text. Later, when you feel you have mastered the relaxation response, you could switch to the format of thinking the directions to yourself in your practice sessions.

Imagery The word *imagery* is usually associated with a visual experience—imaging a picture in the mind's eye. Imagery can also include other modes of internal experience such as auditory, gustatory, olfactory, and tactile modes. One or more of these modes can accompany visual images. Most people can create a visual experience in the absence of an actual physical perception of something. For example, if you speak to someone by telephone, you may automatically conjure up a picture of that person at some level of your awareness. When you give directions to someone on how to carry out a nursing procedure, you may be describing the procedure from a mental picture. Daydreaming is another common form of imagery. Your experience with the guided imagery about the lemon in Chapter Two is yet another form of visualization and illustrates how images can affect our bodies.

Three categories of imagery are (1) spontaneous, such as fantasy and dreams; (2) reconstructed or memory images, which may take an eidetic or very clear, detailed form; and (3) guided, such as those used in biofeedback to give suggestions to oneself for control over bodily states. All three of these types can be used to calm the body, elicit the relaxation response, and heal the body of stress-related "dis-ease." Images, positive or negative, trigger emotional reactions, which lead to changes in our bodies, either of a stressful or calming nature. According to Achterberg and Lawlis[14], our right-brain hemisphere is predominant in imaging and in the processing of emotional information as well as in directly influencing the autonomic functions of the body. This means our bodies can respond more easily to pictures in our minds than to verbal commands alone. How can we apply this information to creating and maintaining a relaxed body state?

To use imagery as a method of passive relaxation, get yourself in a comfortable position, whether sitting or lying down, and close your eyes. As in other exercises, make arrangements so that you will not be interrupted. Turn on soft music if it is not distracting. First visualize pictures that calm you on a mental, emotional, and spiritual level. These may be nature scenes—beautiful mountains, trees, or beaches. Let yourself see the details so vividly that you feel you are actually there. Breathe slowly and regularly as you see these images and notice any relaxation that occurs. You may also want to visualize calming colors and let yourself feel as if you are floating safely and calmly in these beautiful colors. Next you may wish to use visual similes or metaphors to enhance relaxation. These can be created by visualizing what your body or parts of it remind you of. For instance, perhaps you see your arms and legs as pieces of cooked spaghetti, or your whole body as a lily pad on gently rippling water.

Relaxation is also possible by visualizing body parts and systems. See in your mind's eye the muscles in your forehead going limp and peaceful or joints relaxing and being at ease or your stomach lining secreting just the right amount of acid at the right time while muscles in the stomach wall tighten only when necessary for digestion. Try imaging your blood circulating easily throughout your body with no blocks or barriers to its flow.

Another way to create a physically relaxed state is to visualize your entire body either at rest or in action in a calm, graceful, peaceful state. View your body as if you are outside it watching it function perfectly in as relaxed a state as you can imagine.

You may want to start practicing relaxation imagery first in formal practice sessions. As you master the technique, these images will become part of your mind/body consciousness, constantly helping you to relax.

Meditation   Meditation is a method for handling stress at physical, mental, emotional, and spiritual levels of our consciousness. Shapiro defines meditation as "a family of techniques which have in common a conscious attempt to focus attention in a non-analytical way, and an attempt not to dwell on discursive, ruminating thought."[15] Hundreds of styles of meditation are taught around the world. Some produce states of quiescence and peace while others generate states of excitement. In this section attention will be focused on ways to promote physical relaxation. As with other relaxation methods, meditation reduces messages from inner and outer stressors, which keep the cortex of our brains alert. By reducing stress, muscles can relax and homeostasis can be regained.

A mindfulness type of meditation in which you let yourself respond to stimuli without becoming attached to them can be used for body relaxation. To practice this process, sit or lie comfortably with your eyes closed. Allow your awareness to focus on your body in a general way. Notice sensations of tension and relaxation as they emerge and recede from your awareness. Let yourself be free of judgmental thoughts about your observations—just become aware of one sensation after another in an easy flowing manner. The nonjudgmental awareness of your body will allow it to automatically relax and restore energy. This meditation, if practiced faithfully, can build a subtle awareness that keeps the relaxation process going while you are attending to other matters.

One of the best-known physical relaxation meditations is Benson's relaxation response [16], a mantra-type meditation. The Benson method will be described in some detail in Chapter Five when we deal with anxiety.

Physical relaxation is often associated with breath meditations, which are thought to relax muscles, oxygenate the body, and bring prana or energy into the body. Three styles of this meditative process are described below.

When practicing breath meditations, lie on a fairly firm and flat surface. First you may want to try a breath awareness meditation. Begin by lying on your back with your eyes closed. Notice how your chest and abdomen move as you breathe. You may find it helpful to place one hand on your abdomen and one on your chest. Simply keep your awareness open to observing your breathing for a few minutes. After doing this you may want to deliberately breathe abdominally. As Swami Rama points out[17], breathing diaphragmatically is the most important aspect of breathing. He believes chest breathing, as most of us are inclined to do, is part of the fight or flight syndrome and engenders tension and anxiety. Diaphragmatic breathing is calming and steady and so relieves tension. If you wish to practice diaphragmatic breathing, remain in your supine position, and as you inhale, let your abdomen rise and lower ribcage expand. As you exhale, let your abdomen move toward your spine. Your chest does not need to move much, but the middle and upper lungs should be oxygenated as well. Disciplined practice of this manner of breathing will help you make it a relaxing habit. Though it is more difficult to practice while sitting in a straight chair, doing diaphragmatic breathing practice in this position can help you get in the habit of deep breathing while sitting.

Another form of breath awareness meditation is to spend a few minutes practicing deep abdominal breathing while focusing on the air as it moves in and out of your nostrils. Maintaining your awareness of this process amounts to using a concentrative form of meditation to relax.

Yet another often-used breath meditation is breath counting. This will be described in detail in Chapter Five. It, too, is a concentrative method of eliciting a relaxation response. Finally, a method that I have discovered to be helpful is one I call "circle breathing" meditation. To practice, get comfortable and begin deep abdominal breathing. Now imagine a circle and let your breathing follow the outline of the circle so that you breathe steadily with no stopping after inhaling or exhaling. Go slowly and be careful not to hyperventilate. Practicing this can be relaxing and, at the same time, help you learn to keep breathing rather than to hold your breath in stressful situations.

Body Movement for Relaxation   Yoga, bioenergetics, the Feldenkrais method, and Tai Chi are examples of this way of reducing tension by body movement.

The practice of yoga originated in Hindu philosophy and is directed toward union with the Supreme Consciousness. Several systems of yoga are still taught today and Hatha Yoga is most relevant for physical relaxation. Body postures, called asanas, and breathing exercises help reduce tension and improve flexibility. Many books are available that illustrate asanas and describe the breath control training. You may find an instructor helpful when beginning your study of this method if you are not familiar with this type of exercise.

Bioenergetics is a body awareness and exercise method that helps people relieve chronic tension, thus making possible a higher energy level in the body and mind. Alexander Lowen has written several books on this subject, including *The Way to Vibrant Health* [18], in which he and Leslie Lowen describe the standard exercises, which are similar to yoga postures but involve more strenuous movement. Some massage techniques are also employed in this method of relaxation.

In his book *Awareness Through Movement* Moshe Feldenkrais [19] presents the theory and practice of his method of body relaxation and integration of the body and mind. The exercises he has designed are thought to improve posture, increase breathing capacity, develop coordination, and relieve tension. Feldenkrais further contends that through self-education about one's body and its movement a more complete self-image will evolve. This expanded self-image enables a person to deal with present events in a less distressed manner.

Tai Chi Chuan is· a Chinese form of exercise to gain optimal health and tranquillity. It is concerned with movement as a way to relieve tension and regenerate energy as needed. The gentle, nonforced motions help keep the body and mind flexible and resilient. Circular motion is emphasized, and the body is kept balanced and calm. Breathing is an important part of the graceful motion of Tai Chi. The book *Embrace Tiger, Return to Mountain*[20], an edited transcript of a workshop Huang led at Esalen Institute, describes many Tai Chi principles and movements. As with other body movement exercises, a teacher may be very helpful in the early stages of study and practice.

Hands-on Methods of Relaxation   Ashley Montague in his book *Touching* describes studies of gentled animals as compared to controlled animals, which were not stroked or handled. He concludes that the "gentled animals respond with an increased functional efficiency in the organization of all systems of the body."[21] Nurses are familiar with clinical situations in which the touching of clients leads to great relief and release of tension. Often, however, a person who is accustomed to being the one who touches does not arrange to *be* touched. We will now review methods of passive relaxation which involve being touched. The list includes massage therapy, acupressure, reflexology, touch for health, and healing by touch.

Massage is an ancient healing art. It is practiced today by certified massage therapists who manipulate muscles, ligaments, and connective tissue to stimulate the circulatory, lymphatic, and respiratory systems while relaxing muscles and releasing tension. Many injuries and dis-eases can be helped by means of various massage techniques.

We have noted that chronic muscle tension and spasms are major reasons for feeling exhausted when under stress. Massage therapy can effectively reduce prolonged muscle contractions so that mobility, flexibility, and energy are restored. I am fortunate to have an excellent massage therapist working with me in my professional practice and teaching, and have found her work with clients to be an important part of their return to health. Most often, a massage prior to a session with me allows the biofeedback and psychotherapy to progress more quickly than it might have done if a massage was not performed. When people are physically relaxed, they do not employ their psychological defense mechanisms to as great an extent as they do in their usual stressful states. Many clients have exclaimed after a massage, "So this is what being relaxed feels like!" The experience certainly varies from one massage therapist to another, but basically massage therapy provided by a caring professional can result in a great sense of restoration and relief from destructive tension.

Acupressure, or Shiatsu, is an Oriental massage in which the fingers are pressed on acupuncture points along meridian lines through which energy flows in the body. See Figure 20 for a front view of meridian lines. Pressing on these points, or tsubo, allows energy which has been blocked by some kind of distress to move again, relieving pain and tension. Relaxation and tranquillity are common outcomes of a Shiatsu treatment. As with certain types of massage techniques, acupressure can be somewhat painful for the moment when pressure is applied, but the sensation is of "comfortable" or "useful" pain, and, overall, the experience is energizing and relieves pain. Wataru Ohashi's book on Shiatsu [22] gives some theory and many illustrations of tsubos and how to practice Shiatsu. Though it may take years of study to

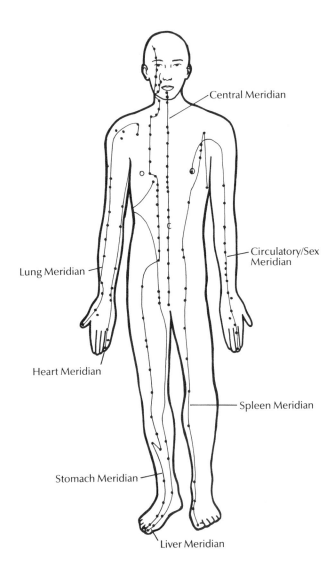

Figure 20: Meridian lines depict channels of energy flow through the body. (Adapted with permission from E. P. Dutton, Inc.)

become proficient, it is easy to learn some of the more common techniques.

Foot Shiatsu, or pressing the tsubos on the sole of the feet, is also called reflexology or zone therapy. This method is based on the theory that the reflex points in the feet correspond to organs in certain zones of the body (or along certain meridians). Pressing these points, then, may release blocked energy and affect whatever parts of the body are along that line or in that zone. For instance, according to Eunice Ingham, who wrote two classical books on reflexology [23], to relieve a tension headache one can press the reflexes to the seventh cervical spine area which are located on the outer aspect of the side of each large toe between the base and the toe joint. Then turn the toe from side to side a few times. Reflexology can also be done on the hands. Thus a similar point on the thumb would be used for treatment of a tension headache originating in the neck area.

Touch for health is another system based on relieving tension and pain by working with acupuncture points and meridians. In his book *Touch For Health* John Thie [24] describes how to test and strengthen muscles along meridian lines. When a muscle tests stronger after treatment of an acupressure holding point or tracing a meridian, it is assumed that the energy is unblocked. With this treatment, like others just described, comes a sense of relaxation and revitalization.

Another group of hands-on therapies also relieves distress by working with body energies. This category can be called healing by the laying-on-of-hands since it literally is practiced this way but may or may not have a religious connotation. All of the hands-on methods for reducing tension described so far address theoretically and clinically the concept of life energies or the electromagnetic or whatever other energy fields exist around and in a living body. These energies can be detected with the hands and can be unblocked and redistributed by the "healer." When the energies are rebalanced, a person feels more relaxed. Richard Gordon, in *Your Healing Hands*[25], describes polarity therapy as one hands-on method of healing. Figure 21 illustrates his concept of the life force or energy field that circulates around and through our bodies. Polarity work involves the use of deep massage, light touch, and working with the energy field by holding the hands slightly away from the skin surface. Working in this way allows the psychological value of touch to be combined with energy work, and as with massage, a sense of profound relaxation and peace can occur.

Recognition of the value of hands-on therapies for relaxation and healing is now evident in the nursing profession. Dolores Krieger, Ph.D., R.N., of New York University, has taught thousands of nurses the theory and practice of healing by the redistribution of body energies. This approach will be discussed in Chapter Six.

Integrating It All   We have reviewed many forms of passive relaxation as ways to manage bodily distress, realizing that these methods will relieve distress at other levels concomitantly. If you find that you are not able to relax easily or do not seem to arrange the time to relax even though you feel you want to, stop for a moment and complete the sentence, "I am afraid to thoroughly relax because . . . ." See if you are willing to deal with your reasons and allow yourself the right to be free of damaging tension. Even those of you who clearly prefer an active form of relaxation may want to seriously consider this issue.

If you are well able to practice relaxing and can feel stress-reducing benefits from the practice sessions, your

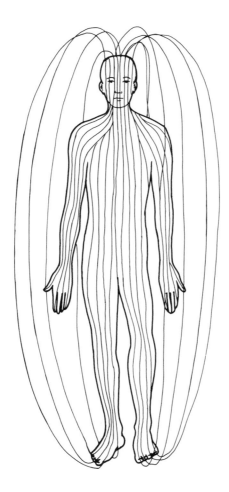

Figure 21: Illustration of Gordon's concept of life force/energy field which circulates around and through our bodies. (Adapted with permission from Unity Press.)

next task is to integrate these skills into daily life so you can stay relaxed and prevent chronic tensions and their ills. As Lazarus states in his article on daily hassles and health, "the small defeats and troubles of our daily lives may cause as much harm as the great ones." [26] The ultimate in stress management is to respond to stressors with an automatic relaxation response as well as to deal with stressors from an unflappable frame of mind.

Even if most of us do not get that far along or do not wish to, we can integrate our ability to elicit a relaxation response into stressful hour-by-hour situations. To do this we need reminders to relax at many intervals during the day. In my practice I provide people with their choice of colors and size of adhesive dots, which mean "relax." People stick these in places at home and work such as on the inside of desk drawers, on calendars, and on the underside of phone receivers so that they are not in sight at all times. When a dot is seen, people do a mini-relaxation response by taking a deep breath, lowering their shoulders as they exhale, and visualizing a calm scene or signs of calmness in the body. The dot may also remind people to take a few moments to sigh deeply a few times, making a sound as they exhale if possible.

This procedure helps people be more aware of tension and need for its release. Those who are interested become increasingly aware of subtle tensions and take immediate action to relax. Eventually, people become more aware of the tension produced when they do such everyday things as walk, talk, read, and eat, so they can do these simple tasks in a more relaxed manner. All of this integration practice provides a hedge against the "hassles of life" we face in so much of our waking time.

Perhaps you have a satisfactory exercise program built into your life already. If not, and you feel motivated to begin exercising, you may want to choose from both the active and passive categories. You are most likely to stay motivated to exercise with regularity if you find the forms of exercise you choose appealing from the outset and experience them as relaxing in some way during or after your exercise periods. If you discover a routine which is not only relaxing but enhances awareness of your body, thoughts, and feelings, you are fortunate for the awareness benefits will be valuable in further promoting your stress management ability in a general sense.

Management of Special Bodily Distress Problems

Bodily distress can come in nearly unlimited forms. The common ones are obesity, pain, and serious diseases, such as cancer, heart attacks, and multiple sclerosis. We will now apply some stress management principles to these problems which are manifested in the body. By this I mean to imply that there may well be psychological and spiritual origins to the problem, but we will discuss these ideas in later chapters and limit ourselves right now to bodily stress management of three problems: obesity, pain, and cancer.

Obesity   People often overeat to cope with stressors. Logically, then, one would expect that when people learn to relax, be assertive, and feel self-confident, the pattern of overeating will disappear. Meanwhile, there are some relaxation and imagery methods that can be helpful in weight regulation.

Deliberate deep muscle relaxation by any of the methods described earlier can help minimize the emotional components of the drive to eat when under stress. Many of my clients place one of their adhesive dots on the refrigerator so that they are sure to relax when they see it and take time to consider whether eating is right for them at that moment. If it is, they eat. If not and they eat anyway, no self-punishment is required. If it is not the right time to eat and they turn away from the food, they congratulate themselves and visualize themselves as full, slim, attractive, energetic, self-confident, or whatever positive images they enjoy most.

Regular practice of imaging some very pleasant setting or memory and then imaging healthy, low-calorie foods and finding them satisfactory may be helpful. Occasionally, I make a cassette recording for people to play before meals as a guided imagery rehearsal of that experience. The general idea is to relax, imagine a very happy memory or situation, and then visualize eating in a very detailed manner (for example, seeing oneself eating small bites slowly, smiling, chewing carefully, and enjoying the flavor). The imagery continues on into the time after the meal when people visualize themselves as full, jovial, content, and thin.

Another way of using imagery is to spend three periods of five minutes each day relaxing, creating a happy mood, and seeing oneself very clearly in the body shape desired. This picture begins to permeate one's consciousness so that it is easier to make choices consistent with one's "reality."

Pain   Bodily pain is one of the most distressing experiences possible if it is severe or chronic or both. In my practice I have seen many people with migraine headaches. Though the treatment is holistically oriented, I will describe only the portion that involves biofeedback and imagery. The usual biofeedback method employed is hand warming. Often clients with migraine headaches will have very cool skin surface temperatures of their hands. The basic task is to (1) learn to warm the hands, (2) learn to keep them warm while awake and working, and (3) warm the hands drastically if getting a signal that a headache is beginning. If the hands are warmed at the earliest point of onset of a migraine, the headache can be aborted.

How can the hands be warmed at will? Sometimes when people are connected to a biofeedback thermal instrument, the feedback will be that the temperature is going up and they focus on what they are "doing" to allow this to happen. Perhaps they had just thought something like "I want my hands to warm now" and the body responded to this "command." If automatic warming does not occur, we try various images of warm hands, such as visualizing oneself holding a warm object or having the hands in warm water or seeing the hands appearing to be flushed. Soon one or more images or thoughts will result in feedback that the hand is warming. Often the autogenic phrase "my arms and hands are heavy and warm" leads to steady warming. The more this skill is practiced, the easier it becomes to hold a passive intent in mind and get results quickly.

Using relaxation and mental imagery to relieve chronic pain demands somewhat different approaches. Electromyograph biofeedback may be useful to train tense muscles to relax in spite of the pain. I often make a tape tailored to the client's personality, ability to concentrate, and type of pain. Hundreds of hypnotic suggestions are possible to include on a pain tape. For instance, after some initial suggestions for deep muscle relaxation, images of the pain as a color (people usually see it as red) which is being exhaled and replaced by a soothing color can be utilized. Images which require a person to clearly define the boundaries of the pain and expand, contract, and finally close them down to nonexistence are also helpful. Another category of imaging for pain control is spending time creating images of oneself moving in a pain-free way—perhaps even of taking part in a sports activity to guide the body toward this state of wellbeing.

The other methods of relaxation described in this chapter can be very useful in controlling pain. Some people use imagery of pain relief during a massage. Fortunately, there are many choices about how to use relaxation and imagery with a body in pain.

Cancer   Managing severe bodily distress, as in the case of metastasized cancer, often involves pain control methods similar to those just described. Another aid to bodily distress is desensitization therapy. This therapy is discussed in Chapter Five and is useful for people who react with major bodily distress to chemotherapy treatment.

The process of relaxation and imagery can be used to attempt to alter the course of the cancer itself. In 1977 I took a formal training program with Carl and Stephanie Simonton, who wrote, with James Creighton, the book *Getting Well Again*[27]. Much of the Simontons' work is based on research that indicates a relationship between stress and a depressed immune system as discussed in Chapter Two. One of the treatment strategies, then, is to help people become psychologically able to manage their lives without weakening their immunologic defenses. The Simontons use imagery as a possible method of activating the immune system and a person's intent to become well. This approach is controversial since there are no hard data to indicate that imaging has an effect on either the immune system or one's attitude toward getting well. Presently there is no biofeedback instrument that can measure the number and types of new white cells being formed in a given time period. If one existed, it could be used to discover the effects of imagery on the immune system. Meanwhile, clinical experiences with people who practice imagery and do become cancer-free are interesting and frequent enough to become a topic of research.

In my own practice I inform clients with cancer of anything I view as of possible help. I am careful to follow their lead after that regarding their interest in attempting to use imagery to influence their immune system. This kind of imagery work is not for everyone since for some it may only be another expectation raised with guilt and failure feelings engendered as death comes closer. Often people find it interesting and helpful as a way of understanding their struggle over living or dying, while others claim it was the main factor in their remission.

In this chapter we have explored ways of assessing and managing various forms and intensities of stress on the body. Fortunately, there are many effective self-help methods, ranging from eating carefully to imaging clearly. Now let's move on to study the mental and emotional aspects of successful stress management.

REFERENCES

1. Hilts, P. "The Clock Within." *Science 80*, December, pp. 61-64; 66-67.

2. Hilts, P. "The Clock Within." *Science 80*, December, pp. 61-64; 66-67.

3. Luce, G. G. *Biological Rhythms in Human and Animal Physiology.* New York: Dover Publications, Inc., 1971.

4. Brintzenhofe, S. *Nutrition During Stress.* Unpublished paper, 1981. (Available from 12623 Laurie Drive, Silver Spring, MD 20904).

5. Ballentine, R. *Diet and Nutrition—A Holistic Approach.* Honesdale, PA: The Himalayan International Institute, 1978.

6. Ballentine, R. *Diet and Nutrition—A Holistic Approach.* Honesdale, PA: The Himalayan International Institute, 1978.

7. Bland, J. *Your Health Under Siege: Using Nutrition to Fight Back.* Brattleboro, VT: The Stephen Greene Press, 1981.

8. Brintzenhofe, S. *Nutrition During Stress.* Unpublished paper, 1981. (Available from 12623 Laurie Drive, Silver Spring, MD. 20904).

9. Mandell, M., and Scanlon, L. *Dr. Mandell's 5-Day Allergy Relief System.* New York: Pocket Books, 1979.

10. Anderson, B. *Stretching.* Bolinas, CA: Shelter Publications, 1980.

11. Kuntzleman, C. T., and editors of Consumer Guide. *Rating the Exercises.* New York: William Morrow and Company, Inc., 1978.

12. Jacobson, E. *Progressive Relaxation.* Chicago: University of Chicago Press, 1929; *You Must Relax.* 5th ed. New York: McGraw-Hill Book Company, 1978.

13. Rosa, K. R. *You and AT*.* New York: E. P. Dutton & Co., Inc., 1976. (*Autogenic Training)

14. Achterberg, J., and Lawlis, G. F. *Bridges of the Bodymind.* Champaign, Ill: Institute for Personality and Ability Testing, Inc., 1980.

15. Shapiro, D. H. *Meditation.* New York: Aldine Publishing Co., 1980.

16. Benson, H. *The Relaxation Response.* New York: William Morrow and Company, Inc., 1975.

17. Rama, S., Ballentine, R., and Hymes, A. *Science of Breath.* Honesdale, PA: The Himalayan International Institute, 1979.

18. Lowen, A., & Lowen, L. *The Way to Vibrant Health.* New York: Harper and Row, 1977.

19. Feldenkrais, M. *Awareness Through Movement.* New York: Harper & Row, 1972.

20. Huang, A. C. *Embrace Tiger, Return to Mountain.* New York: Bantam Books, Inc., 1973.

21. Montague, A. *Touching.* 2nd ed. New York: Harper and Row, 1978.

22. Ohashi, W. *Do-It-Yourself Shiatsu.* New York: E. P. Dutton & Co., Inc., 1976.

23. Ingham, E. D. *Stories the Feet Can Tell.* Rochester: Ingham Publishings, 1938; *Stories the Feet Have Told.* Rochester: Ingham Publishings, 1951.

24. Thie, J. F. *Touch for Health.* Marina del Rey, CA: DeVorss & Company, 1973.

25. Gordon, R. *Your Healing Hands.* Santa Cruz, CA: Unity Press, 1978.

26. Lazarus, R. S. "Little Hassles Can Be Hazardous to Health." *Psychology Today*, July 1981, pp. 58-62.

27. Simonton, O. C., Matthews-Simonton, S., and Creighton, J. *Getting Well Again.* Los Angeles: J. P. Tarcher, Inc., 1978.

CHAPTER 5

Stress and the Mind

Our minds are probably the major personal mediating factor influencing style and effectiveness of managing stress. We use our minds constantly to perceive, evaluate, and react to life circumstances. In this chapter we will examine the relationship of our mental and emotional states and stress. More specifically, we will examine methods of assessing, preventing, and managing the distress that both originates from and affects our mental and emotional states. Refer to Figure 22 for an account of the mind as a personal mediating factor within the general conceptual model. As you can see, the word *mind* encompasses both mental and emotional capacities that relate to each other in a feedback loop. This loop illustrates that our emotions influence our thinking, and our thoughts affect and often determine our emotional states. Once again, it is important to remember that stressors do not cause illness. What matters is how we use our personal mediating factors, in this instance our minds, to cope, since our minds greatly influence the probability of our staying well or becoming ill.

What is the mind? In this chapter I define it as the thoughts and feelings, new and accumulated, which form values, belief systems, and attitudes. Behavior usually reflects the functioning of the mind, and in combination, the two can be called our personality.

How does the mind function in response to stressors? First, it perceives a stressor from sensory data collected through the nervous system and, at times, from what could be called parasensory or intuitive data. It then translates and evaluates the information for degree of threat through the higher cortical functions of the brain. This mental functioning leads to some degree of intensity or emotional arousal through stimulation of the limbic system and hypothalamus. Another common way for the mind to function in response to a stressor is for the emotional part of the feedback loop to be aroused through the pathways of the reticular activating system. This in turn triggers cortical or mental functioning in response to the stressor.

As the central nervous system receives bits of information collected from such sensations as touch, vision, and hearing, and from our intuitive "sense" of things, it perceives the information and assigns some meaning to it. The process of perceiving and evaluating allows an infinite number of possibilities for distorting "reality." The greater the level of distress, the higher the probability of distortion. Perceptions and evaluations in ordinary as well as in stressful states are influenced by unique characteristics in each person's genetic makeup and life experience. Each person has certain physiological pre-

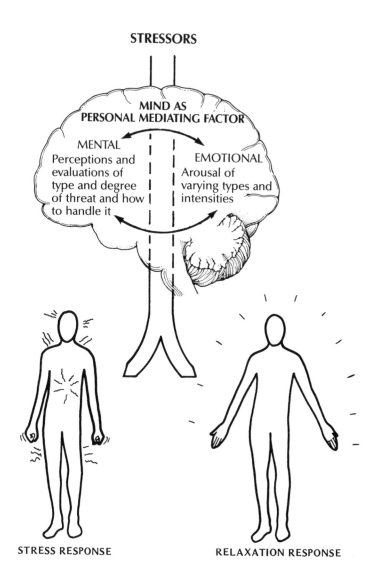

Figure 22: Illustration depicts how the mind serves as Personal Mediating Factor in relation to stressors.

dispositions and biochemical endowments that influence the perceptual and evaluative process. Also influential are life experiences such as positive and negative childhood events; experiences that have been particularly powerful reinforcers of certain ideas, feelings, and behaviors; self-concept and self-esteem; psychological defense mechanisms built up over the years; attitudes and belief systems; and particular cultural and social influences.

There is no limit to the range of possible choices in how to perceive and evaluate "life data." These choices are critical in determining stress levels and thus a person's progress toward wholeness.

Mental and Emotional Manifestations of Stress

Now let's take a more detailed look at how the mind manifests signs and symptoms of distress. It is important to understand that the mental and emotional signs and symptoms of distress are in themselves stressors so that a snowball effect is possible once the distress has begun.

Signs of mental and emotional dysfunction become clear when a person has candidly responded to personality inventories, such as the Minnesota Multiphasic Personality Inventory or tests that give information about the individual's state and trait anxiety and sense of internal and external control of his or her life. The assessment inventories used in this chapter are not standardized psychological tests and are intended to be used only to gain a greater degree of awareness of signs of mental and emotional distress in yourself and in your clients.

While almost any mental/emotional state can be related to stress, not all are caused by it, so we must carefully differentiate which signs are caused by stressors and which may be derived from other problems such as brain tumors or an injury or genetically determined dysfunction that affects the central nervous system. Accurate judgment in differentiating a stress-determined illness from a central nervous system disease is extremely important. Tragic errors can be made in assuming that some mental/emotional or physical manifestation of distress has been caused by a dysfunction of the mind without checking thoroughly into the possibility of organic causes. I recall an example of this when, as a student nurse, I was assigned to a psychiatric inpatient unit where a man who claimed to be physically disabled and nearly paralyzed was labeled as having a conversion reaction. The staff assumed that a stressful incident with his wife had triggered a condition that mimicked multiple sclerosis. The treatment indicated that he must care for himself totally. When he fell out of his wheelchair to the floor, he had to crawl on his stomach to get to the restroom or his bedroom or to the dining room. If he did not make it to the dining room on time, he did not receive any food. This client was sure that he actually did have multiple sclerosis and that the stress of the treatment was contributing to his deterioration. Later he was diagnosed definitively as having multiple sclerosis! At that point, of course, he did need some psychotherapy to help him let go of the distress and bitterness he felt from his experience on the psychiatric unit.

Signs and symptoms of mental/emotional distress can range widely in form and intensity. For instance, a person may feel mildly dejected and sad or may experience severe suicidal depression resulting in death. Mental and emotional signs of distress can be internally felt and not easily observed. They can also take the form of behavioral dysfunctions that are quite easily recognized. Basic internal feelings that are manifestations of distress are sadness, fear, anxiety, guilt, anger, and apathy. The sadness may, as was mentioned, develop into a suicidal depression or a depression of any intensity and is often connected with unfinished grief. Fear may be mild and acute or it may develop into a clearly differentiated phobia, which may severely interfere with a person's life.

Anxiety is very closely associated to the fear response psychophysiologically. Anxiety, however, may be free-floating, lacking attachment to one identifiable object. You may be accustomed to feeling anxiety as nervousness, confusion, worry, and a feeling of being overstimulated. This can progress to a sense of having too little time to accomplish one's goals, a sense of disorganization, forgetfulness, difficulty in making decisions, difficulty sleeping, and even some disorientation for time and place. Finally, "life" seems out of control. Perhaps you have experienced moments in which you have had no substantial sense of coherence about life.

Another characteristic of anxiety is a feeling of powerlessness to gain control. One good indicator to watch for in determining the sense of powerlessness of yourself and others is the phrase "makes me" used as an attribution of power to "forces" over you. For instance, you may have said, "My supervisor makes me sick" or "That staff meeting made me have a headache" rather than "I feel sick when I am around my supervisor" or "I give myself a headache during staff meetings." The latter examples provide a more accurate account of where the responsibility lies.

Another internally experienced sign of distress is the feeling of guilt. This, too, can take many forms from mild to severe. Mild guilt may simply help you accept your share of the responsibilities of a shift's work. Severe guilt, however, can lead to repressed anger and psychophysiologic problems.

Anger as a sign of distress comes in many forms as well. You have surely experienced times of being annoyed, irritable, and resentful of others. Perhaps you have not experienced the other end of the spectrum, which would be an out-of-control rage. Perhaps you have experienced some form of rage that you were able to control and are not frightened of losing control of your anger.

Last, perhaps appropriately, is apathy. Going through motions in life but feeling empty and uncaring on the inside can be a sign of mental and emotional distress.

Besides basic feelings going awry as a sign of distress, there are also other emotional syndromes that are combinations of basic feelings and are evident also as signs of distress. Examples are frustration, lowered self-esteem, and loneliness. Frustration occurs when we have set a goal for ourselves, whether it be to attain a master's degree or to purchase a certain item at the grocery store, and that goal is blocked. A sense of momentary or prolonged immobilization, helplessness, anger, sadness, and anxiety may result, varying in intensity, which may not always reflect a linear relationship to the apparent importance of the goal. For instance, you might experience more frustration over not being able to find curry powder at the grocery store when you need it for a dish you are preparing than if you suddenly have the realization that you cannot afford to attend a graduate program in the fall. A lowered self-esteem is also a combination of many basic feelings and can range from a lack of full appreciation of yourself to a lack of respect for yourself or even pure self-hate. Loneliness is also a combination of many feelings, such as sadness, fear, and anger, and is associated with a poor self-esteem and frustration. Depression and loneliness are often not-so-strange bedfellows.

Having reviewed internal experiential signs and

symptoms of distress, let's turn now to dysfunctional behavioral signs of distress. Again, these can range from mild to severe forms. Be aware of any of your own past or present experiences with these dysfunctions as well as relating these to your clients. First is compulsive behavior, which can take a myriad of forms from compulsive patterns having to do with perfection and pleasing others to more symbolic forms such as compulsive handwashing. Sexual dysfunctions are quite common as a sign of mental and emotional distress, since a decrease in available energy and interest can lead to fear of unsatisfactory performance and consequent rejection. Once anxiety is built up about sexual performance, old fears and guilt feelings may re-enter the picture as well. Another behavioral sign of mental and emotional distress is a psychophysiologic disorder such as those we have already thoroughly reviewed. Yet another graphic sign that can be a manifestation of high distress is an acute psychosis. Strong feelings of unreality and inability to communicate with others can arise immediately after an experience of extremely high distress or after a prolonged period of intense distress. Last is addictive behavior as a reflection of attempts to handle either specific stressors or a generalized sense of distress about life or both. In my clinical practice, the courses I teach in stress management and meditation, and in consultation with corporate and government groups, I have found that some degree of substance addiction is common rather than unusual. By *substance* I mean anything from caffeine and cigarettes to drugs and alcohol. Obviously, some addictions are of more concern than others, but the tendency toward addictive behavior is, in itself, a sign of poor coping behavior and vulnerability to distress. Substance addiction today is still a largely unrecognized problem.

Self Assessment of Mental/Emotional Stress

In Chapter Three the Holmes and Rahe Life Change Inventory and other tools were used to identify relevant stressors. In this section we will utilize a number of formats to help you determine your predominant coping patterns in terms of cognitive style, personality style, and life style. At the end of this section, if you have fully participated in the suggested exercises, you will have a fairly comprehensive profile of your own methods and patterns of coping with mental/emotional distress. You will be able to see how many of these coping styles are functional and how many are dysfunctional in managing the stress of your daily life.

Cognitive Style of Coping   Let's turn first to your particular cognitive style as a way of coping, specifically your style of dealing with:

- negative thoughts and feelings about yourself and others
- control issues
- strong emotions
- goal setting
- frustration

These categories are some of the most common areas in which cognitive processes can go awry.

Assessing the Process of Coping With Negative Thoughts and Feelings About Myself and Others   Negative attitudes toward ourselves and others often will trigger a stress response. Following are two sets of questions designed to help you heighten your awareness of your coping style when dealing with negative thoughts and feelings. Take the time now to thoughtfully answer the questions. As you do this, feel free to add to the list any other descriptions you may think of to more exactly describe your special ways of dealing with negative thoughts and feelings.

When I have thought, said, or done something I regard as stupid, crazy, bad, or a sign of imminent senility, I:

	Always	Sometimes	Never
Cry or at least get tearful	___	___	___
Laugh it off	___	___	___
Meditate	___	___	___
Get depressed for hours or days	___	___	___
Tell others how bad I am	___	___	___
Forgive myself cheerfully and immediately	___	___	___
Feel guilty for not being more adequate	___	___	___
Isolate myself from others and sulk	___	___	___
Forgive myself if I promise not to do it again	___	___	___
Feel frustrated that I'm not perfect	___	___	___
Punish myself in some way	___	___	___
Try to obtain sympathy for my inadequate performance	___	___	___
Quickly do something else equally bad	___	___	___
Blame someone else	___	___	___
Read something inspirational	___	___	___
Excuse myself saying I was under stress at the time	___	___	___
Eat, drink, smoke, or swallow a pill	___	___	___
Do some physical exercise	___	___	___
Relax and try to think rationally about what's happened	___	___	___
Start "biting people's heads off"	___	___	___
Talk with someone I trust to get another perspective	___	___	___

	Always	Sometimes	Never
Pound my fist on a wall and scream	___	___	___
Start thinking no one will ever be able to love me	___	___	___
Shrug it off as an unimportant thought	___	___	___
Change the negative thought or feeling to a positive one	___	___	___
Seek professional help	___	___	___
Know that at least if no one else loves me, God does	___	___	___
Other _____	___	___	___
Other _____	___	___	___

When I have negative thoughts and feelings toward others, I:

	Always	Sometimes	Never
Tell them exactly what I think immediately	___	___	___
Pout and hope they catch on	___	___	___
Take a swing at them	___	___	___
Speak authoritatively to them about how bad they are	___	___	___
Try to ignore my thoughts and feelings	___	___	___
Threaten to report them to someone	___	___	___
Smile and forgive them	___	___	___
Punish them by refusing the next favor they ask	___	___	___
Tuck the thoughts and feelings away so I can remember them clearly years from now	___	___	___
Stop speaking to them	___	___	___
Criticize them for something unrelated to what I am upset with them about	___	___	___
Blame them for my negative reaction	___	___	___

	Always	Sometimes	Never
Calmly share my thoughts and feelings, taking full responsibility for these	——	——	——
Send an anonymous note to express my thoughts and feelings	——	——	——
Wait for an apology	——	——	——
Imagine various punishments of all degrees for them	——	——	——
Cut off the relationship with no explanation	——	——	——
Try to understand why they acted as they did	——	——	——
Demand an apology or other compensation	——	——	——
Say a prayer for them	——	——	——
Hope they have an accident or suffer in some way	——	——	——
Rise above my ego bruise and let go of my negativity	——	——	——
Scream at them	——	——	——
Let some time go by, then reexamine my thoughts and feelings	——	——	——
Figure they will get what they deserve without my intervention	——	——	——
Seek professional help	——	——	——
Rally a group to support me against them	——	——	——
Have an accident or become ill	——	——	——
Take action soon to improve the situation	——	——	——
Figure the whole thing is not worth the effort of dealing with it	——	——	——
Other _____	——	——	——
Other _____	——	——	——

The scales you have just utilized will help you heighten your awareness of your typical ways of coping with negative thoughts and feelings about yourself and about others. Glance back over your answers to see what your most frequent type of response is to negative thoughts.

Assessing My Patterns of Dealing With Control Issues
In a group, whether family, social, or institutional, struggles for control and power go on at some level. In our American culture, historically and in the present, we take pride in having the freedom to control our own lives. At times, however, particularly when we are in a position of power professionally as the "strong helper and director," we may try to control others' lives as well. There are times, of course, when this can be beneficial, such as when a client is unconscious; however, attempts to control others are often similar to walking across the Grand Canyon on a tightrope since both can be a very slippery business with high distress consequences if all does not go well.

Perhaps you can remember some of the struggles you experienced in your childhood about your own autonomy. Remember particularly some of the authority problems you may have experienced as an adolescent. Do you recall saying, "You can't make me do it"? Do you still feel this way toward certain people in your life? Your rank in the family as only, oldest, youngest, or middle-range child probably had a great influence on your attitudes and behaviors concerning control issues. Various styles of attempting to gain control develop out of whatever position we grew up in. What methods did you learn to be particularly proficient in as a child for getting control of a situation? Do you still use these methods? Perhaps your early years left you with some degree of insecurity, which leads you to want to have control over yourself and any situation you are in so you can feel safe. Generally speaking, are you in least distress when you are in control of a situation or when you have a sense of flowing along with it?

What is your current pattern of dealing with control issues when an authority figure is involved? Do you nearly always acquiesce? If so, do you feel good when you do or are you resentful and think you should have spoken up to get your point of view across? Or do you almost always resist an authority figure's ideas? Are you good at backing up your resistance with many reasons (or possibly excuses), or do you "forget" to carry out the instructions of an authority figure?

How do you relate to peers when control issues arise? Do you take pride in yourself for being "easy to get along with"? Do you typically think of yourself as being in a parental or caretaking position with most of your peers? Do you typically think of yourself as deserving nurturing from them most of the time?

Do your patterns of dealing with control issues vary according to whether you are dealing with well or sick people? Do you generally just take care of everybody? Are you more assertive in establishing control with people who are ill?

After considering the above questions, name three typical ways you handle control issues. Write these down on your assessment sheet. Do you think these three ways usually lead to distress or stress reduction?

Assessing My Patterns of Dealing With Strong Emotions
Let's search out typical ways you deal with strong feelings. Again, take enough time to think and learn about yourself. To assist you, I have provided a "complete the sentence" tool. If you are already overdosed on self-evaluation, take a break or read some other section to reduce your distress; otherwise, continue by spontane-

ously filling in the following blanks with your typical thoughts and/or feelings and/or actions as illustrated in the sample:

When I am feeling ANXIOUS, I

   take a walk

   try to discover the reasons

   feel guilty

Now fill in whatever words or phrases seem appropriate in describing your reactions.

When I am feeling ANXIOUS, I

_____

_____

_____

_____

_____

When I am feeling AFRAID, I

_____

_____

_____

_____

_____

When I am feeling GUILTY, I

_____

_____

_____

_____

_____

When I am feeling SAD, I

_____

_____

_____

_____

_____

Now review your answers. What are your predominant ways of handling strong feelings? Do these match some of your responses to previous questions about your coping patterns? Are you beginning to get a clear picture of these patterns?

Assessing My Goal-Setting Style   Setting goals too high or too low or not at all can lead to an insidious kind of stress reaction. That reaction is often experienced early as a vague discomfort and gradually becomes focused enough for us to know it as something like "What am I doing with my life?" Some external event like the children leaving home or an unfavorable change at work usually helps crystallize this sense of concern at various times in our lives. Take a few minutes now to do the following exercise:

Write one goal in specific behavioral terms next to each of the following times:

Today _____

Six months
from now _____

One year
from now _____

Five years
from now _____

Retirement _____

Did you find you are already aware of or have set forth your life goals? If so, does having goals increase or decrease your stress (or both)? Do you find it more or less stressful to forget goals and "go with the flow"? How will you handle your frustration if your goals cannot for some reason be achieved? How will you handle frustration if the "flow" heads for a black hole?

Assessing My Patterns of Coping With Frustration   Now let's investigate more thoroughly how you handle frustration. Frustration, as we said earlier, is the usual emotional reaction when a goal is blocked and becomes temporarily or permanently unattainable. Many of the assessment tools already described can be utilized in determining your reaction to frustration, particularly those pertaining to negative feelings and control issues.

To gain a more complete picture of your patterns of coping with frustration, let's utilize some guided imagery. Read the instructions. Then close your eyes and let yourself clearly imagine the scenes.

Imagine you are walking fairly quickly and purposefully down a path. You are on your way to a once-in-a-lifetime event which you have been looking forward to for a long time. Suddenly an object or a person blocks your path. What or who is blocking it? How do you handle this situation? Many ways

may occur to you. Let them become clear and remember them when you are finished.

Did you reach your goal? Write down any new knowledge of frustration and patterns you noticed yourself
using. Add these to your list of discoveries or rediscov-
eries so far and carry on!

Personality Style of Coping With Stress   Now that we
have rather thoroughly examined your cognitive style of
coping, let's see if you have enough energy and fortitude
to explore your personality style (this section is easier).

First, consider Figure 23. This is a rough sketch of
three common ways of reacting to stressors. Each line
drawing, resembling Selye's description of the physiological stages of the general adaptation syndrome, represents in this case personality styles instead of physiologic styles.

Style 1 people have a low alarm threshold and are
hyperexcitable, getting alarmed very quickly and to a
high degree. People with this style may be in the stage
of resistance for a prolonged time, experiencing their
rush of adrenaline as proof of being alive or as being
familiar at least. I call people who are stuck in this style
the alarm/resistance junkies since they seem to "need"
to be alarmed-aroused. This style may be associated with
simple hyperactivity, hysteria, and occasionally psychosis.

Style 2 people are within a normal range in each
stage. The degree of alarm matches the type of stressor,
the resistance is not unpleasant but not sought out, and
the exhaustion is a useful recovery period. Rather stable,
well-balanced people have this profile.

Style 3 people have a high threshold of arousal and
are not notably different from one stage to the next.
People who are extraordinarily defended in a psycho-

PERSONALITY STYLES OF COPING WITH STRESS

Style 1.
Personality has low threshold for alarm and maintains arousal (resistance). Difficulty with exhaustion stage—either "crash" or do not relax before going into another alarm stage.

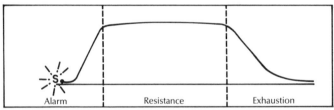

Style 2.
Normal range of responses. Alarm is appropriate to stressor. Resistance lasts no longer than necessary to handle stressor. Exhaustion is a productive part of process and allows restoration.

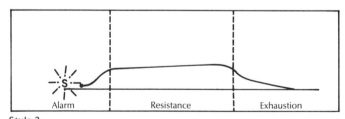

Style 3.
Very slow and minimal degree of alarm. Resistance is low arousal type. Exhaustion is slow and quite complete.

Figure 23: Patterns of personality responses to stressors.

logical sense or who are barely, for whatever reasons, aware of themselves and their environment will manifest this kind of line drawing. People with this style could be simply apathetic, depressed, or maybe withdrawn from reality in a catatonic way.

Now that you have examined these possibilities, see which you relate to most easily and then draw your own line of response as you think your personality ordinarily reacts to stressors. You may want to think of several of your clients' personality styles in this respect as well.

In further surveying your personality style of coping, glance through the following brief descriptions of Type A and Type B behavior as presented by Friedman and Rosenman[1] in their book *Type A Behavior and Your Heart.*

Type A

- Moves, walks, and eats rapidly
- Is highly impatient with self and others
- Does two or more things at one time
- Is preoccupied with self in thought and conversation
- Experiences guilt if relaxes several hours or days
- Does not take time to observe environment
- Has a constant sense of not having enough time
- Challenges and competes with others
- Uses muscles spasmodically and has obvious muscle tension
- Believes success is due to ability to work quickly
- Translates and evaluates self and others in numerical terms

Type B

- Is free of all Type A behaviors

- Has no time urgency sense
- Has no impatience
- Is not preoccupied with self and achievements
- Plays for fun, not necessarily competition
- Relaxes without feeling guilty
- Relaxes while working

Again this is an opportunity to classify yourself in a very general way. Most of us are somewhere along a continuum between Type A and Type B. Friedman and Rosenman suggest that you ask those close to you who know you well to help you determine whether you are more a Type A or Type B. Doing this will give you a chance for some valuable feedback. I've been amazed occasionally in my clinical practice at how entirely different the client's spouse or significant other reports the client to be regarding coping behaviors that the client has reported. That information is often of crucial importance in determining a program of therapy.

The third way of evaluating your personality style regarding stress management is to see if your style involves dependency as a theme. If so, the second question is to what degree and how does this pattern create additional distress?

We can be dependent upon anything or anyone and often this can relieve distress. There may be times, however, when we become too dependent upon another person or upon a substance. At that point we or others become uncomfortable. Too much dependency implies that something is missing from ourselves—that we are not whole.

To help you assess your dependency style, we will use alcohol as an example, realizing that alcohol is still one of the most common substances used to help bolster mental and emotional coping skills. If you do not drink, simply substitute whatever you may be dependent upon and see if you are managing your dependency in your best interest.

Following is a checklist made up of a combination of questions I have used in clinical practice and questions outlined by Alcoholics Anonymous. Before you fill out the checklist, let yourself try to be open to the possibility that you are addicted. As you know, the person who is addicted is highly resistant to that label, preferring to think that he or she simply enjoys alcohol or any other substance and could moderate it or stop at any time. Not true.

SUBSTANCE DEPENDENCY CHECKLIST

	Yes	No
Alcohol helps me to relax better than anything else	——	——
I drink to help me forget my worries for a while	——	——
I really enjoy the pleasant feeling alcohol gives me	——	——
Sometimes I sneak a few extra drinks	——	——
Alcohol helps me get rid of sad and angry feelings	——	——
At times I drink alone	——	——
Alcohol helps me feel more confident and at ease with people	——	——
I feel less frustrated after drinking some alcohol	——	——
I stopped for a whole month once but started again	——	——
Alcohol helps me feel less guilty	——	——
I like myself better after a few drinks	——	——
My spouse said I am drinking too much	——	——
I feel less lonely when I drink	——	——
Sometimes I have a drink to start the day	——	——
Occasionally I lie about the amount I drink	——	——
I pretty much rely on alcohol to help me cope with stress	——	——
Sometimes I switch from one form of alcoholic beverage to another or only drink after lunch and later	——	——
I sometimes miss appointments for work		

or participation in a family activity
because I was drinking   ___ ___
I envy people who can drink and not black
out or have other difficulties   ___ ___

Answering "yes" to only a few of these may mean that you are alcohol dependent or addicted to whatever substance you were testing. If you are, you probably do not believe this statement or are beginning to feel defensive at this point. If you have any notion that you may be addicted and wish not to be, there are probably many resources available in your own community. For further information on Alcoholics Anonymous, write to P. O. Box 459, New York, NY 10017, or consult your telephone directory. Some of the suggestions for managing distress later in this chapter may also be of help in minimizing or halting dependency on a substance, person, or situation.

Life Style and Managing Stress   Cognitive style, personality style, and now life style—these are perspectives from which to view your reactions to stressors. In this section you will be offered guidance in standing back and observing your own life style—the way you organize your life. We will pay particular attention to social interaction management and time management as areas to assess for patterns you use to cope with stress.

In Chapter Three we delved into your social systems' memberships, roles you play, changes at this level, and energy gained or lost in a social context. In this assessment section, we will pay attention to your social life style. For instance, are you gregarious in nature? Do you find life less stressful if you spend most of your waking hours with others? Or do you find people generally stress-producing and prefer to be alone much of the time? Perhaps your preference has influenced the area of nursing you practice. Are you a nurse who comes in contact with people, or do you carry out research, which involves time alone to read and think?

Often when I ask professional women in my practice or my course in stress management and meditation to use the twenty-minute tape, *Suggestions for General Relaxation,*[2] two to six times each day (admittedly a somewhat outrageous request!), they are alarmed and often declare that they cannot possibly find twenty minutes to be alone even one time each day. This is especially true of those who have children and work full time. Most of these women have never seriously considered withdrawing from their social environment except to sleep. Many have reported not even having private time in the bathroom at home! These women, largely nurses, lawyers, and management level government workers, report feeling incredible time and responsibility pressures. Often they are trying to be perfect wives and mothers as well as perfect professionals.

Those who are successful at being able to practice the tape two times each day express amazement at the rather foreign and pleasant sensations of relaxation. Running a close second is their amazement at being able to get unstuck from their overstimulated social life styles and have a sense of control again over the amount of contact they make with others. Does this vignette fit your own style? Would you, too, be horrified at the idea of listening to a twenty-minute relaxation tape alone two times a day? If so, you may be letting your boundaries be too permeable so that people feel they can call you or drop in on you or make demands on you any time and you will respond positively. Perhaps you stay engaged in social circumstances even though you would like to be alone. We will take a closer look at managing social overstimulation later in this chapter.

At the other end of the spectrum is social isolation. Solitude, of course, can be very restorative and productive if it is voluntary, under your control, and time-limited. Solitude can be vital, and it may be rich in meaning. It does not necessarily mean understimulation. Being alone, however, can be highly stressful if the aloneness is not by preference and you long for contact with others. During my early 20s I was on bedrest at home, in intractable pain, and diagnosed as being terminally ill. Dying in a nursing home in a few months or years was the predicted course of events for me. In spite of being married and having wonderful friends, everyone worked full time and I was usually alone all day. While I needed some solitude, I also felt at times too much aloneness at that crisis point. Perhaps you have had a similar experience to help you understand more clearly how much and what kind of aloneness and lack of stimulation you find restful and how much is stress-producing. Some people cannot tolerate being at home alone even for three days with the flu! Think how lonely it might be, as some of our clients show us, to be basically alone while dying slowly of cancer. Boredom, depression, and loneliness can be serious stressors from social understimulation. Take a few minutes now to examine your own past and current life for feelings of boredom and loneliness or just plain lack of exciting social stimulation. Are you involved enough with others to form a mutual support system to get each other through crisis situations or are you a loner taking the risks of that life style?

How is your balance between overstimulation and understimulation? Are you growing and resting at satisfactory rates? Do you have a sense of peace and contentment about your social life style?

The other area of assessment of life style as a way of coping with mental/emotional stress is time management. How well do you manage time? Is this a large or small part of your total stress profile? Listed below are a few statements about time management. See to what degree they apply to you.

- I almost always feel rushed.
- I am so busy handling crisis situations that I don't think to get other work done.
- Sometimes I have minor accidents from hurrying too fast.
- Often I cannot remember what someone said because I was in a hurry and did not listen carefully.
- I get irritable easily over issues having to do with time.
- I go through yellow traffic lights.
- When someone is late to pick me up I get very angry.
- At times I feel almost totally overwhelmed by time deadlines at work and at home.
- I try to do most things myself.
- Usually I don't say no to requests or demands.
- I feel guilty if I'm not pressed for time.
- I feel purposeless if every hour is not full.
- I rarely prioritize my activities.
- I would not want to be lazy like some people I know.
- Making every minute efficient is the most important thing in life.

Take a moment now to write a brief note on your

ability to manage time.

This concludes the section on assessment of mental and emotional patterns of coping with stress. Keep your profile handy to use as you read the next section of this chapter.

Managing Stressors By Managing the Mind

In this section, as in others on managing stress, we will discuss both prevention and management of acute and chronic distress. Changes, particularly losses of many different kinds, can trigger patterns of stress which are experienced mentally and emotionally and must be dealt with mentally and emotionally.

There are some fairly well established ideals for using the mind well to manage stress. One of these ideals is for a person to have the opportunity to work out past stressful issues which trigger off thoughts, feelings, and behaviors in one's present life leading to perceiving and evaluating in a distorted, stress-inducing mode. Another ideal is that people would be guided to develop ways of utilizing the mental abilities to creatively prevent and manage distress. The third ideal has to do with the actual steps of the process of reacting effectively with the mind to stressors. It goes something like this: First, the bodily sensations would be accurate. Second, the perceptions would be full and clear. Third, the person's evaluations would contain no distortions of "reality." Fourth, the person would be aware of many viable alternatives for reacting to the stressor immediately. Fifth, the person would be able to make a balanced decision about what action to take, using an integrated combination of rational and intuitive abilities. Sixth, the person would be able to spontaneously and effortlessly take action to remedy the situation and restore him or herself to a homeostatic state. Now back to everyday reality.

Look over your assessment work and identify typical ways you cope mentally and emotionally with stressors. Which of the following categories do your coping strategies fall in most frequently?

1. Avoidance of stressors.
2. Accommodation to stressors.
3. Regulation of mental/emotional reactions to stressors.

Once again, any of these categories can be healthy or can be taken to an extreme and result in distress for oneself and/or others. Balance is an important variable in determining how healthy the outcome will be. The rest of this chapter will be devoted to suggestions for healthy mental and emotional management of stress. We will explore avoidance of stressors and accommodation to stressors, but will emphasize self-regulation of reactions to stressors.

Avoidance of Stressors   Denial is a mental process that effectively blocks stressors from conscious awareness. Denial has very limited usefulness in dealing with stressful events. One example of healthy denial, however, is familiar to you if you work with people who have been diagnosed as terminally ill with cancer. Those who do not deny having cancer but do deny the inevitability of death seem to maintain hope and live more active and satisfying lives than those who accept the prognosis fully and become depressed. There are also people, of course, who do not employ denial and go on to die gracefully and peacefully. Generally speaking, the use of denial as a way of dealing with stressors is ineffective and can even prove to be dangerous.

Withdrawal as a mental mechanism for coping also

has limited but occasional usefulness. Withdrawal from stressors for a time can be highly efficacious if staying in contact with the stressors is inducing more distress and slowing the resolution of the problem. For instance, withdrawing from a worrisome problem for a while by reading the newspaper, going to a movie, or taking a walk may allow you to develop a new perspective and solve the problem upon returning to it. Similarly, taking a break from a spirited argument or from the frustration of figuring your taxes may be a useful form of temporary avoidance. A longer withdrawal from people in your life who are steadfastly stuck in patterns involving constant demands on you or criticism of you may also be stress relieving. This may be accomplished by physically withdrawing and/or emotionally detaching so that you do not take the demands or criticism too seriously. Physically withdrawing so that mental and emotional withdrawal is possible can become a habit involving continuous change of jobs and relationships. You are likely to be familiar with the famous "geographical cure" utilized by people who change locations often as a dysfunctional attempt to withdraw from stressors.

Unfortunately, some people find mental and emotional withdrawal so relieving that they begin to automatically withdraw from stressful situations. You can see that, with the way things go some days, this would amount to withdrawing from life itself!

Accommodation to Stressors   Accommodation is the talent of living in a stressful environment, getting distressed, then handling that distress. It is an attitude of adapting, of "hanging in there and taking it." The focus of the person who accommodates is not so much on changing the stressors or avoiding them but on handling the tension as it builds up. A very old man said to me once about his marriage, "Oh, I don't know if after 58 years we really love each other. We argue a lot and I think we've just gotten used to each other. If I get too mad I just go down to my tool shop in the basement and work for a while." His tool shop helped him accommodate to his perceived stressors.

People who accommodate try to let off tension and regain a homeostatic state so they can return to the stressful situation for another round. (Does this remind you of your work life?) Sports, hobbies, intoxication, and confrontation of another are commonly utilized to discharge tension so accommodation can prevail.

Accommodation can be healthy but it can also be a neurotic or even a psychotic way to cope with stress. Sometimes needs conflict or ambivalence prevails, and accommodation is chosen over less stressful choices. A common example of this, which has decreased some since the advent of the Women's Liberation Movement, is the wife who says, "I know he drinks too much and he beats me sometimes, but when he is sober he is a nice guy. Besides, I don't think I could make it on my own financially."

On the other hand, accommodation to some situations may be necessary. You may decide to care for a retarded child, a dying spouse, or an elderly mother in your home even though this provides a highly stressful living milieu at times. A friend of mine accommodates to her dying mother's incessant demands on her and criticism of her by reducing her tension through gardening, verbalizing her feelings to a few friends, and reading spiritually inspirational books at her meditation time each day.

Regulation of Mental/Emotional Reactions to Stressors
Probably the most fruitful way of using our minds to

manage stress is to gain more control over our responses to stressors. By gaining control I mean allowing full awareness of the stressors and of our reactions to them and changing these reactions if they are troublesome to us. This method of managing stress does not preclude the use of avoidance and accommodation methods when they seem better suited to the situation. Also, though this method is not aimed at changing others, we know from systems theory that when one person changes him or herself, others change in reaction to the difference in that person. It is very likely that self-regulation will, in a sense, "cause" others to change although no direct energy has been expended for that purpose.

In this section we will investigate possibilities for self-regulation of:

- beliefs about ourselves, others, and life generally;
- emotional responses to stressors;
- knowledge and experience, particularly in the areas of decision making, goal setting, and time utilization.

Keep your assessment list handy or the results clearly in mind so that you can pay particular attention to those discussions most relevant to your ways of managing stress. As you read and think, you may want to jot down ideas for modifying your old stress management patterns and adding new ones.

Before launching into the details of controlling our stress states by modifying our beliefs, emotional responses, and knowledge and experience, I want to briefly discuss the creative process. Creativity allows us great flexibility and choices in our life. Creativity is an important concept to be aware of since it is valuable in helping us overcome our natural resistance to changing ourselves. Creative approaches, such as using fantasy and imagery, the relaxation response, and meditative methods, help make change less painful or even fun. Many creative methods such as these allow us to stretch our potential to its farthest dimensions, bringing in new energy and power needed for supporting the change to new thoughts, feelings, and behaviors.

Fantasy, imagery, and the relaxation response, as well as some meditative methods, have been discussed in Chapter Four. Using these methods to help regulate your mental and emotional reactions to stressors is suggested because these methods allow new beliefs, feelings, and knowledge to emerge from within you so that your options for reacting to stressors can be increased tremendously.

Some people believe that meditation is simply a way to avoid stressors or escape from them. This is a very naive opinion, apparently based on lack of experience with this method. Meditation can be a highly efficient and effective method of self-transformation. Our reticular activating systems allow a meditative state and in this state we can focus our minds in a special way. This focusing and the inner silence can help us restore energy, increase our self-awareness, heighten our sense of our own wholeness, detach us to some degree from our problems, and enhance our intuitive abilities so that we can solve problems and deal with stressors much more easily than those with comparable coping skills who do not meditate.

As you read the rest of this chapter, which focuses on self-regulation, see if you can maintain an openness to changing yourself in some or many ways. Allow yourself to experience a sense of excitement about the creative possibilities for change in some of your typical patterns of reactions to stress. Your use of this book will be most enriching if you pause to practice some of the suggested exercises so that you can actually experience some shifts within yourself rather than expecting change to happen totally at an intellectual level.

Self-Regulation of Beliefs   As we have noted previously, most of our emotions and behaviors stem from our belief system or philosophy of life. This belief system can be consciously verbalized to some extent, but also lives within us in the form of constant monologues and dialogues that are not always within our scope of awareness. Although we may not always be aware of it, we are often feeling and behaving in ways that reflect our beliefs about ourselves, others, and life in general. The more negative beliefs we hold, the greater chance we have of experiencing negative emotions and exhibiting negative behavior.

In reworking our belief systems so that they support a positive experience of life and, therefore, a less distressing experience of life, it is not necessary to change all our negative beliefs to positive ones. Indeed, a few negative beliefs can help create a stress level that is invigorating, motivating, and rewarding. The idea is not to turn yourself into a modern day Pollyanna, but to transform the negative beliefs that cause distress. When working with your beliefs in the following section, the basic question to ask yourself is, "Does this belief help me manage my stress?"

Cognitive behavior therapists, such as Ellis and Harper,[3] Beck,[4] and Burns,[5] believe that in most instances our thoughts induce our feelings. Ellis and Harper describe the ABC theory of rational-emotive therapy as follows:[6]

A = Activating event or activating experience
B = Belief system about A
C = Emotional consequence

Let's apply this ABC theory to stressful experience. The first step in resolving the situation is to become clearly aware of the stressful context, that is, the activating event or experience that triggered the stress response. Next is to become aware of your belief system about the event or experience that triggered the stress response (such as, "I don't believe people should act that way"). Sometimes these beliefs can be difficult to bring clearly to mind. Beck[7] refers to the thoughts that manifest our belief system as "automatic thoughts." When these automatic thoughts lead to distressing emotional consequences, as in the ABC theory, it can be assumed that these thoughts were somehow distorted and tend to lead to self-defeat. For instance, perhaps the automatic thoughts predicted catastrophe, were overgeneralized, negatively evaluative, exaggerated, or illogical. Burns[8] in his book *Feeling Good* lists ten common cognitive distortions. When applied to your automatic thoughts, they can aid you in discovering how your thoughts may be hazardous to your health. Burns' list of cognitive distortions is as follows:[9]

- All or nothing thinking
- Overgeneralization
- Mental filter
- Disqualifying the positive
- Jumping to conclusions
- Magnification (catastrophizing) or minimization
- Emotional reasoning
- Should statements
- Labeling and mislabeling
- Personalization

A negative thought may have one or more of the cognitive distortions represented in it. We will look at examples of these cognitive distortions throughout the rest of this section.

Now let's apply some of the cognitive behavior therapy theory to your belief system about yourself. You would be a highly unusual person if you had no cognitive distortions to cause self-doubt about your own worth and your own power. Women particularly seem vulnerable to cognitive distortions of a self-denigrating nature. An important point to keep in mind when looking at negative thoughts you may have about yourself is that this thought is *your opinion* and does not reflect some sort of ultimate reality.

Let's take a look now at a practical approach to enhancing self-worth beliefs so that you are less vulnerable to the kind of distress that has its origin in threats to your self-esteem. We will use what Burns calls the "double-column technique" [10] in which you write your automatic thoughts in the first column and your rational responses in the second column. Figure 24 illustrates the double-column technique. Other labels for the columns have been added to give you choices of how to conceptualize the thoughts that go in these columns. Two examples are given to illustrate typical stress-inducing type statements about the self and suggested stress control thoughts that can be substituted for the thoughts in the first column.

Take some time right now to do this exercise so that you can train yourself to be more aware of your self-critical thoughts and learn how to substitute useful thoughts for the harmful ones. You might begin by jotting down some typical self-putdowns that you are aware of saying or thinking in the course of a day. Another way to try to identify the self-critical thoughts is to think about the times you have been distressed and imagine what self-critical thoughts you might have been thinking that helped create your distress. Often our self-

DOUBLE-COLUMN TECHNIQUE

SELF-CRITICISM	SELF-DEFENSE
HARMFUL MONOLOGUE	USEFUL MONOLOGUE
IRRATIONAL STATEMENT	RATIONAL STATEMENT
SELF-DEFEATING STATEMENT	SELF-ENHANCING STATEMENT
STRESS-INDUCING STATEMENT	STRESS-CONTROL STATEMENT
1. I am stupid.	1. I wish I had known the answer immediately to the question he asked. I can learn the facts, if I study them. Stupidity is not a word that applies to my general mental functioning.
2. I am a bad nurse. I get angry at patients and they don't even deserve it.	2. Getting angry at patients does not make me a totally bad nurse. I don't snap at all patients. I get angry at times when I am particularly distressed and I am working on managing my distress so that won't happen.

Figure 24: Slight modification of Burns' double-column technique. (Adapted with permission from William Morrow & Company, Inc.)

critical thoughts will be subliminal in nature so are not entirely at our conscious memory level. This is why you may have to imagine thoughts or give your "best guess" as to what these distressed thoughts could have been. In analyzing the distortions involved in these self-critical thoughts you may want to refer back to Burns' list. These definitions of cognitive distortions overlap a bit, so avoid being too precise—just get the general notion of what the problem is or describe the distortion in your own terms.

After discovering the distortion(s) involved, go ahead and create a self-defense or rational statement and check this statement for any cognitive distortions. If none is obvious, practice saying out loud or thinking about the statement in column 1 and then quickly substituting the statement in column 2 so that you begin the process of thinking differently about yourself. Since this is a re-training process and takes practice, you may want to write down some of the stress-inducing statements and their stress-control statement counterparts on index cards and carry them with you so you can practice substituting self-enhancing statements for self-defeating statements when you are in situations such as waiting for someone to meet you or standing in line at the bank or grocery store. As you practice this exercise in re-training your thinking about yourself, keep in mind that regular practice is necessary to change thought processes. If the practice is going well, you will begin to be highly aware of your self-defeating statements and become more adept at substituting rational or self-enhancing statements. A major reward for this work will be a gradually increasing sense of self-acceptance and respect, which can be invaluable in supporting you during times of upheaval as well as supporting you through daily interactions and events that could threaten your self-esteem and self worth.

As you practice becoming more aware of self-critical thoughts and revising them, you may notice images and memories that tell you something about how you are bringing old blows to your ego into your daily patterns of thinking. For instance a client of mine, Ann, who raised a family and returned to school to study nursing, complained tearfully about what a poor student she was. When the test results came back, however, she usually had earned an A and sometimes a B. Upon discussing this we found that Ann, in her grade school years, had been labeled a poor student and had many automatic thoughts about herself that she applied inappropriately to herself in her present school situation. We also discovered that she was comparing herself only to the very few people in her class who consistently got the highest scores on tests and was not comparing herself to the people who were getting C's, D's, and F's. Ann was able to train herself to stop herself each time she was aware of thinking she was a poor student, see that statement as an old self-defeating one, and focus her thoughts on her actual present achievements instead. Once this process was learned, she found attending school a much less stressful endeavor.

The practice of affirming your belief that you are a worthwhile person can be done in many ways. One method is substituting a useful statement for a harmful one, as Burns suggests. Another method is to choose brief, positive self-statements from the second column and say or think these brief statements to yourself many times each day. Once you begin this process you may find that other self-affirming phrases emerge, such as, "I am healthy," "I am relaxed," "I am joyful," "I am content." To some people this seems like a "positive brainwashing procedure." It is a conditioning process designed to help you overcome the destructive influence of previous negative conditioning processes in your life that have trained you irrationally to think badly of yourself.

If you sit quietly to do some self-affirmation exercises, you may notice some spontaneous mental images appearing with some or all of the affirmation statements. Do pay attention to these images. They are powerful ways for your mind to influence itself. For instance, let's say that the affirmation, "I am joyful," seems ridiculous to you, especially in thinking of yourself as being joyful at work. If you allow yourself to picture yourself being joyful at work, however, you may eventually come upon a visual image that is highly appealing to you and also quite possible for you to achieve. If you retain this mental image of yourself being joyful at work, you may find yourself spontaneously creating that experience or you may recall the image while you are at work and deliberately create a situation in which you can be joyful.

Our beliefs about our own power as a person are highly important in determining how we will manage stress in our lives. If we see ourselves as weak and without influence, we leave ourselves open to being easily threatened and distressed. If, on the other hand, we are behaving in a responsible way, we will see ourselves more appropriately as powerful people who can usually attain even more power and influence with others if we desire that. A crucial point is whether we feel in control in some basic way of our own lives and actions.

Next comes the question of how much power we wish to have or wield with others in our environment. We all have the choice of thinking and behaving as if "they" have all the power and are in control because "they" are bigger, smarter, or have more money than we do. You may recognize this as the way many nurses think of doctors. That way of thinking, in which the locus of control is external to oneself, can lead to serious stress problems. An alternative is being aware of and responsible for the power you have to essentially create your own world of life experience. This usually leads to a much more hopeful and actually powerful way of living. Behaving in a powerful way, of course, also increases the probability of being viewed and respected as a powerful person by others.

Beliefs about our own personal power can be influenced by studying and practicing assertive behavior. Herman, in her book *Becoming Assertive*, defines assertive behavior as:

> that type of interpersonal behavior in which a person stands up for her or his own legitimate rights in such a way that the rights of another are not violated. Assertive behavior is a direct, honest, and appropriate expression of one's feelings, opinions, and beliefs. High-quality assertion also includes an empathic component that shows some consideration, but not deference, for the other person.[11]

You can see that assertive behavior is very different from aggressive behavior in which a person stands up for his or her own rights but may be uncaring or even cruel to the other person involved. Aggressive behavior usually indicates that the person is afraid of losing control over someone else. Nonassertive behavior often indicates a fear of losing love or approval. Assertive behavior helps us to have respect and love for ourselves and control over ourselves in interpersonal situations.

A philosophy of rights of human beings can help overcome hesitation to behave in an assertive manner and can help overcome guilt at having been assertive if this behavior is new and seems too bold. Alberti and Emmons[12] in their book *Your Perfect Right* list what they call the Universal Declaration of Human Rights, which is a detailed reminder of things such as "All human beings are born free and equal in dignity and rights"[13] and that we have the right to freedom of thought and freedom to express our opinions and freedom to free ourselves from any cruel or degrading treatment by others. They also make the point that in our society we tend to make assumptions about some people being "better" than others so that it has become acceptable for employers to treat employees badly or doctors to treat nurses badly or teachers to treat students badly. Think for a moment about your own rights. Do you believe you have the right to express your thoughts and feelings, the right to say no, the right to suggest that changes be made in your workload or work environment, and that you have the right to free yourself from being treated with disrespect? What other rights can you think of that you feel are yours but you may not have acted on them as much as you would like?

Let yourself imagine right now, with your eyes closed, yourself acting on one of these rights in an assertive, but not aggressive, manner. Let the image focus clearly enough in your mind so that you have the sense that you have actually practiced the assertive behavior that reflects one of your beliefs about your personal rights. The more clearly you can practice this in imagery form, the more likely you will be to apply it to your daily circumstances.

Both verbal and nonverbal behavior are important when practicing assertiveness. Verbally, it is important to keep breathing deeply enough to support a moderate, firm, and strong voice tone which is not too emotional in character. Try right now saying the word "no" in an assertive versus a nonassertive or an aggressive manner. Breathe deeply enough to support your tone and imagine some request being made of you to which you are calmly and firmly saying no. Beginning sentences with "I'd like . . . ," "I want . . . ," "I don't want . . . " is an effective way of speaking because it is direct and genuine. Using a verbal format, such as "When you _____, I feel _____," helps avoid blaming another person for your feelings while still getting the connection between his or her behavior and your feelings across in a clear manner.

Basic nonverbal considerations for behaving in an assertive way include again supporting yourself well by breathing deeply and regularly, making eye contact that is as comfortable as possible, letting your facial muscles express whatever feelings you are verbalizing, and being aware of your posture so that you are either standing or sitting upright or leaning slightly toward the other person. Let's try another quick imagery exercise right now.

> With your eyes closed, imagine clearly some recent stressful situation in your life, either at work or at home, and replay this situation in three ways. First, let yourself imagine that you behave in a nonassertive way, that you practically whisper, look at the floor, and generally slump over as you're talking. Second, let yourself imagine that you respond in a highly aggressive way, perhaps even glaring, shouting character-assassinating words and phrases at the other person, and looking a bit physically threatening. Third, try visualizing yourself being calmly secure in your confidence that you are in control of yourself and can get your points across very clearly and easily to ensure that you are heard.

Which of the three scenes did you enjoy most? Did you become aware of certain kinds of rewards that might accompany each of the three scenes? Which of the three alternatives provides you with the best results in terms of both short- and long-range goals? Perhaps you can be free now to imagine more than one scene in which you assert yourself successfully and minimize distress.

We have discussed many elements of the importance of beliefs about oneself. The second major section pertaining to beliefs is concerned with our beliefs about others. Whether we harbor negative feelings about others or express them aggressively, we create distress for ourselves. The more we can let go of irrational negativity toward others the less distress we will experience. Learning to be assertive with others may help stressproof your attitudes toward others. Confidence in your own worth and power and rights is also essential. Distress seems to come when our thoughts about others contain distortions; for instance, we might expect too much of someone or apply our "shoulds" to them, or have a tendency to see people in a prejudicial light.

To become more aware of some of the interpersonal cognitive distortions we may be using without awareness, let's go back to Figure 24 and substitute the word "other" for "self" in "Self Criticism" and "other" for "self" in "Self Defense." Take a few minutes now to write down some of your favorite complaints about other people in column 1. Look these over for cognitive distortions and write a corrected sentence or phrase in column 2. After doing this, see if you think it would be appropriate to say this corrected sentence to the other person at some point. Imagine yourself carrying this out and imagine what the results could be.

Besides our beliefs about ourselves and others, we also interact with others based on our general beliefs and philosophy of life. Antonovsky [14] writes about our ability to perceive the world as coherent. He defines the sense of coherence as follows:

> . . . a global orientation that expresses the extent to which one has a pervasive, enduring though dynamic feeling of confidence that one's internal and external environments are predictable and that there is a high probability that things will work out as well as can reasonably be expected. [15]

In other words, a person with a strong sense of coherence recognizes the complexities of life, but feels that life is comprehensible and predictable and also has a sense of confidence that, in the long run, things will work out well. Antonovsky relates this sense of life as coherent to the ability to cope with stressors, that is, the stronger the sense of coherence, the more adequately people cope with the stressors of any given moment in life. To what degree do you have this sense about life generally? Are you able to see that, indeed, few things have "cosmic significance"? Are you able to be secure enough in your sense of coherence about life to see some humor, even in the most stressful of situations?

Let your mind wander and lightly skim over your life to date for highly stressful times. Can you see that even though the results of these stressful times may not have been exactly as you wanted them to be, in the long run your life has some theme of things turning out well? If you can grasp some of this sense of coherence about your own life, try mentally flashing to that sense the next time you are about to react in a stressful way and see if recognizing your own sense of coherence about life will help you get a better perspective on that particular stressful event.

Self-Regulation of Emotional Responses

There are many ways to regulate emotional responses. Some ways, such as denying, suppressing, or repressing feelings, can lead to psychophysiologic problems and interpersonal problems as well. You may have first-hand knowledge of how difficult it is to deal with someone, for instance, who smiles even though he or she is obviously angry. Numbing ourselves to our emotions is not usually a beneficial way of regulating these responses.

Fortunately, there are many ways to regulate emotional responses. The first step in being able to regulate an emotion is to be very keenly and accurately aware of what we are feeling. Second is being able to accept that emotion instead of denying, projecting, suppressing, or repressing it. Third is being able to evaluate the emotion for intensity and appropriateness to the situation and then being able to express the emotion assertively. In this section we will be paying attention to the emotions and emotional states that are stressful, either because they are part of a stress response or serve as triggers for increased distress. We will pay attention to many ways of dealing with a negative emotional state as well as ways to prevent or at least decrease the probability of experiencing strong negative states that would not be beneficial to ourselves or others.

Our emotional responses usually take place in an interpersonal context. Obviously, whatever we can do to keep our relationships with others healthy will decrease the likelihood of experiencing negative or stressful emotional states. Questions like "How many relationships do I want in my life?" "How close do I want to be to each of these people?" "What do I want from the other person?" "What does the other person want from me?" and "What are the risks I am taking in each relationship?" are important to consider. These questions can be applied to relationships of all kinds, whether they are with clients, friends, or family. Let's turn now to a discussion of dealing with and preventing emotions such as fear, anger and resentments, guilt, anxiety, depression, and sadness, as well as troublesome emotional states such as perfectionism, insomnia, loneliness, addictive behaviors, and sexual problems. Since a book could be written about handling and preventing each of these emotions and emotional states, our discussion of each will be less than comprehensive. I have tried, therefore, to narrow the discussion to include those methods I have found most useful.

Fear   Fear is anxiety with a clear object of focus and can be helpful, even lifesaving, to us. It keeps us, for instance, from jumping out of airplanes without parachutes (or, for most of us, even with parachutes). Cannon[16] described fear and rage responses as both being helpful to cats in coping with threatening situations. Most of our fears are not helpful to us, however, and we are better off without their immobilizing and irrational influence which keeps us from taking risks involved in growth and change. Wolff[17] emphasizes the clinical importance of people fully realizing the "truly poisonous and destructive nature"[18] of such negative emotions as fear and hate on the body.

So how do we deal with and prevent the level of fear that is not lifesaving, but life-sapping? The first step is awareness. As adults we may experience a great deal of resistance to "admitting" we have fears since adults are "not supposed to" have them. Being aware is the vital step, however, to managing fear as a source and sign of distress. Make a list of things you are afraid of, large or small. See if you can allow unconscious fears to become conscious so that you can grapple with them. This can be done by allowing yourself to daydream about fearful situations you have been in throughout your life. Let your mind create images of past frightening events. Write these down quickly so they do not escape back into your unconscious. Perhaps fear images will pop into your mind that do not seem to have actually happened. Treat them just as you would treat a fearful memory. When you recall recent fearful situations ask yourself, "What does this situation remind me of?" Can you see some themes developing? Are you typically frightened of others' evaluations of you, for instance, or losing control of yourself in some way, or of becoming ill or injured? You may want to add to your fear list by letting yourself think of frightening objects or animals and then asking, "What or who does this animal or object remind me of?"

Now that you have your list of fears and possibly some new ones pulled out of your unconscious, what will you do other than stay safe at home rather than go to work today? If you find that fears are a predominant part of your emotional makeup or that you are phobic (will not think of or do some things that arouse fear), you may want to seek some professional help as support and guidance in your progress toward letting go of your fears.

If you want to practice getting rid of old fears, take one that seems to represent a theme or pattern of fears in yourself and let yourself sit quietly, relax, and visualize a clear picture of yourself in a fear-inducing situation. Keep in mind that this is creative work with unlimited possibilities, and let yourself image in detail ways of coping with the situation successfully. Several alternatives may become clear to you. Practice one or more of these solutions until you can feel a shift within yourself away from fear toward confidence and peacefulness. For instance, if a fear of yours is of dealing with the anger or disapproval of others, take a memory of being criticized and see yourself responding in many new assertive, nondefensive, responsible ways. Imagine acknowledging whatever seems true to you about the allegation and calmly add a correction of information, an apology, a statement of future intention, or whatever is needed to resolve the situation to your satisfaction and hopefully to the satisfaction of others as well.

When you can feel less fear during the process of imagining old feared situations, try a "what if" exercise. This involves imagining a future situation that would ordinarily trigger a fear reaction. Staying with our example, perhaps you can imagine your nursing supervisor calling you in to talk with you about a medication error you made and see yourself being able to calmly handle the criticism of your performance. Whatever the content or theme, visualize yourself gracefully moving on through the situation, coping with it flawlessly.

Another way to handle fears and prevent more from developing is to desensitize yourself to your fears. This method is based on the theory of systematic desensitization as described by Wolpe.[19] It works by helping people use a conditioning process to link relaxation with fear or anxiety in such a way that the relaxation response reduces the power of the negative emotional states.

To utilize systematic desensitization on your own fears, choose one strong fear. Let's say it is of giving a speech to the entire hospital or clinic staff or some other professional group. Make a list of several steps leading to the feared event in order of least to most frightening. For instance, in our example, perhaps the least fearful experience is to think of preparing the speech. Next may be imagining that it is two days before the speech.

Next is that you are driving to the location of the speech on the day it is to be given, etc. Take each specific step separately (least fear-provoking first), elicit a deep relaxation response, and imagine the step. When you no longer feel discomfort about one step, go to the next most fear-inducing step and relax through it as well. Be sure to give yourself plenty of time (practicing briefly twice a day for as many days as each step takes) until you can relax on through the final step. In our example, then, the person would feel relaxed even while vividly imagining giving the speech. Each time you practice, be sure you are:

- imagining the appropriate step;
- imagining the scene clearly;
- relaxing very deeply;
- alternating slowly from fear-producing scene to deep relaxation;
- ending on a relaxed, pleasant note; and
- rewarding yourself for practicing.

The desensitization method is one which I have used with clients for fears and phobias of all kinds. I have used this often for helping people with cancer manage the stress of their chemotherapy treatments and have found much success in reducing the intensity of the side effects. The process is as just described. A list is made of the steps that are feared about getting chemotherapy. The first may be going to the car to ride to the doctor's office or clinic and include such items as imagining the odor of the drugs as one enters the treatment area, having the needle inserted in the vein, and feeling the first wave of nausea develop.

Once you have practiced imagining coping well with the feared situation or have been able to deeply relax while imagining yourself in a fearful situation, it is time to practice this in "real" life. Relaxing on through an actual feared situation further desensitizes and helps build confidence. If your fear is still somewhat present in the reality situation, just return to the imagery and practice some more. To be sure how deeply you are relaxing, you may want to consult a biofeedback therapist. I often employ a conditioning process with clients that involves using a biofeedback instrument to help them relax deeply enough to warm their hands into the mid-90s before they do their imagery. They then connect this objective sign of relaxation with success such as "I have warm hands and I am giving the speech with ease" or "My hands are warm and I am taking in the chemotherapy, feeling comfortable with it and helped by it."

Another method of combating fear is to use Burns'[20] two-column method as described earlier in this chapter. In the first column write your automatic fear thought and in the second write the rational response. An interesting sidelight to this is to take your fearful thought and ask "what if" it were true. Keep asking "what if" and reworking your responses into rational statements.

Yet another way of handling fears is to talk about them with others. Support can be gained from finding out that others have similar fears. Sharing ways of coping can be of significant help as long as people are interested in changing rather than simply wallowing in their fears together. At times, telling the feared person him or herself that you are afraid of him or her is an excellent way to explore and eradicate that fear.

The emotion called fear is a basic part of the stressful defense response involving the sympathetic adrenal-medullary system. The more we can control our fears and leave only those that are actually lifesaving, the healthier and more satisfied with life we will be since our threshold for feeling threatened will have decreased, allowing us to proceed through life without so many stressful interruptions.

Anger   Anger, like fear, is involved in Cannon's fight or flight response. For some people it is a way of realizing they are alive. It is sometimes useful in helping us take the necessary action to reach a goal or protect ourselves and others from harm. Generally speaking, however, anger is basically obsolete as a useful, productive emotion since it so often proves to be self-defeating in terms of one's own health and interpersonal relationships. Chronic anger is simply a sign that a person is feeling threatened and distressed. Since anger and joy seem to be unable to coexist experientially, a person is giving up the preciousness of joyful times by taking time to feel anger.

During the encounter group era of the 60s and 70s, a movement arose that helped people become aware of their anger, accept it, and express it assertively. Eventually a twist occurred in the form of a belief that anger in and of itself was good and should be expressed fully and directly without much attention to the effect on the other person (it was the other person's "problem" if he or she was hurt by it). If anger is used in that way consistently, a person can lose the more loving kind of social skills that may have decreased his or her own stress level by bringing people closer in a supportive way. Instead, people are disgusted or frightened and pull away their support.

From a stress theory point of view, saving wear and tear on ourselves is better accomplished by being immediately aware of anger and expressing it in an assertive, effective, responsible way. In this way little or no residual anger will be causing you distress. It is also important to carefully purge yourself of old, suppressed angers that accumulate in the form of resentments, may be conscious or unconscious, and may have an insidiously negative effect on the body. Best yet is the idea of saving much of the energy involved in suppression and fight or flight for some creative purpose. This can be accomplished by changing attitudes and behaviors so that anger is most likely to occur only as is necessary for protection in highly threatening situations.

While some people use their anger in an explosive or threatening way to gain interpersonal power by intimidation, others simply explode as a rather clumsy way of releasing tension. Still others view anger as too hard to control or too frightening to acknowledge within themselves so they suppress it. Some people suppress it for a time and then blow up.

If you wish to manage your anger without suppressing it or exploding into a fight or flight episode, the first step is full and accurate awareness of your anger and its many possible forms. If someone asks you, "Are you angry?" when you do not feel angry, try to stay open to the possibility of being angry and ask what was observed about you that led to the question. Your teeth may have been clenched, your movements abrupt, and voice tone irritable without your full awareness of the anger that was causing these behaviors. Tension in skeletal muscles and hypertension may also serve as clues to buried anger. Bruxism and headaches may be two other signals among many bodily distress signs that anger is presently stored in your body.

An imagery search of the past may also be helpful in bringing your anger to a conscious level so it can be expressed in some way. As with the imagery search for fear, let yourself feel an attitude of openness and acceptance of your own anger as you sit quietly and allow images of angry times in your life to form spontaneously. Write these down as you become aware of them and search for patterns of anger in your life. Often these will involve themes of competition, feelings of having had your territory invaded in some actual or symbolic sense, and feelings of blaming others for treating you in an unfair manner.

What is involved in becoming angry at ourselves and others and then storing these angers until they sour into resentments? The most frequent origins of anger I have seen in clients over the years are:

- A wish for the world to operate in a fair and responsible way.
- Thoughts about how they or someone else should or should not have behaved.
- A wish to be powerful in the control and punishment of others.

Let's look at these sources of anger more closely for your own situation. Again, try to be open to your true feelings and motives and accept whatever you find within yourself about anger and resentment.

First, the possibility that you want others to be fair with you. Defining "fair" is important. Does fair mean how you would have acted? Other people have their own ideas of "fair" since it is a relative, not an absolute concept. As nurses we know that nature is not fair at times. Is it fair that a baby is born retarded or with cystic fibrosis? Fair may be important as a description of our own values to live by, but very easily leads to anger and a fight or flight stress response when we expect others or nature to live by our definition. See if reminding yourself of this general idea will help allay your anger next time it seems based on the "fairness" concept.

The second major source of anger is our "should" or

"should not" thoughts as applied to ourselves or others. Once we have created "shoulds" for others, it is easy to make some irrational meaning out of their behavior and feel angry. For instance, if you think that a friend should have called to see why you were not at work, and because she did not, you believe that she does not "care" about you. This kind of thinking is clearly seen as irrational when you later learn that your friend was at home sick, too!

A third major source of anger results from thwarted attempts to control others which turns into angry, punitive thoughts and actions. Sometimes power over others feels good, especially if we are feeling powerless generally. Perhaps we unconsciously see the world as full of children who need our guidance. This picture leads directly to failure in getting them to "obey," which can trigger much anger. It is easy to go from that point on into punishment rather than calling off our internal dogs and taking a rational approach.

Inherent in all three of these ways of getting angry is the theme of "they make me angry" rather than claiming responsibility for one's own attitudes as the true source of the anger. In many angry situations in your own life, you can see that you had a choice of whether to get angry or not. If you had been able to have more perspective or tolerance or empathy or had not taken a remark personally, you may even have found some of those situations amusing or entertaining in some way rather than triggers for your anger.

When you are already angry, how can you manage your anger effectively and prevent self-destructive use of it? First, let's tackle the problem of exploding from a low threshold for anger or from a habit of holding it in too long. A behavioral bag of tricks to help control this until you can correct it is to delay your response to an incident until you have counted slowly in your head from one to ten, paid brief attention to some other matter, or taken five slow, deep breaths. Another way to avoid exploding is to anticipate an event you would typically respond to explosively and rehearse it either by role-playing or through imagery. Play it out many different ways until you feel you have mastered it and then consciously be as relaxed as possible when actually entering the situation. See if you can think in terms of assertiveness rather than aggressiveness as you work on this.

For the process of looking at and modifying your anger responses as a long-term project, I would suggest two ways of proceeding. One is to get in the habit of thinking of and writing out your angry thoughts. Then think of rational alternatives to these thoughts repeatedly until you feel your thought processes shifting. For instance, the thought, "That client makes me furious; she is nothing but a complainer, intent on criticizing everything," could be changed to "*I* make myself furious; *she* does not" or "There is more to her than the critical side she is showing right now." The second way of working on your anger is to write, for each angry situation of the day, (1) what you will get from being angry, and (2) what it will cost you to get angry. Then repeat this, substituting "staying cool" for getting angry and see what the payoffs and costs would be in that case. Do these exercises regularly each day until you find yourself automatically reacting more rationally to situations. Notice how much your general tension and distress level is dropping.

We all have resentments we have carried from our childhood on. Resentments are angers that are stored, often for many years, in the mind/body. Resentments rob us of energy and interfere with our present ability to think rationally. Resentments also lead to physical illness. Methods I have found useful in helping people shed their resentments often involve role-playing and imagery. Take a few minutes to try the following exercise:

1. First test your willingness to let go of old resentments by imagining one of your resentments as an object you are holding in your hands. See if you can let go of it easily. Hesitant to give up that "power"? Try it again until it is easier to do.

2. Now try playing through a scene that is a source of a particular resentment. See what you can learn from this replay. Either enact the scene or imagine it as it was. Then replay it several times as you create alternatives that would have been in your best interest and perhaps in the other person's best interest also.

3. Try thinking rational thoughts about this scene.

4. Now try imagining what is left of this resentment as an object again. See if you can let go of it without hesitation. Let yourself be aware of any relief you may experience.

The Simontons and Creighton[21] have outlined a way to help people with cancer deal with their resentments. We will use this as the last step in your work with a resentment:

5. Take the resentment you have been using and let yourself picture the resented person. Imagine good things are happening to that person—that he or she is getting just the things he or she always wanted. Note your reaction to this image. If you have difficulty with this it will lessen with practice. Now let yourself take some responsibil-

> ity for what happened between you and the
> other person. See if you can image the problem
> from his or her point of view. Be aware of any
> more relief at this point. Remember, you may
> have to practice these steps repeatedly before
> you can realize a sense of having let go of that
> resentment.

Please keep in mind, as you are working on managing your anger differently and preventing more anger
from accumulating, that these exercises will be effective
only if you are willing to be open with yourself about
your anger and resentment. Motivation to practice regularly is also necessary. As you practice the methods outlined in this section, you may find that you develop
your own particular combination of relaxation, imagery,
and rational thinking that is most effective for you.

Guilt   Guilt is an unpleasant emotion that can be experienced in various intensities. It is a feeling response of
having broken our own or others' rules or codes of behavior. In its neurotic form it is self-hate and distress
stemming from real or fantasied negative acts of omis-
sion or commission. It is depleting or emotionally con-
stricting and lowers the self-esteem since the bottom
line reads "I am a bad person."

In its non-neurotic form, guilt is not a disastrous
commentary on oneself but an acknowledgment of having done something one considers wrong and making
amends if possible. In these instances, guilt seems to be
a rather harmless way of reinforcing ourselves to maintain our own values. If we were able to be all-loving and
empathic we probably would not need this reinforce-
ment process. Meanwhile, non-neurotic guilt, if resolved
quickly, probably does no mental or physical harm.

Distress enters the picture as we slide across the guilt continuum toward the neurotic side. Here we see people who are wringing their hands with self-blame and self-hate. Particularly prone to this distress are those who are obsessed with pleasing other people or following an institution's rules exactly. Some families and religious organizations unwittingly teach people to pay too much attention to rules and link this with children's sense of themselves as good or bad. People with this mental set are highly vulnerable to being manipulated by others since they eventually believe that they are guilty for almost anything that goes wrong with almost anyone. Fear, anxiety, and depression can become part of a neurotic guilt reaction since taking on responsibility for pleasing all people is such a sure way to experience failure.

The first step in ridding yourself of stressful, depleting, neurotic guilt is to be keenly aware of your guilt feelings. Let yourself be relaxed and quiet and think of, or even write down, your own list of things you feel guilty about. Imagine not having any of these feelings. Notice any reluctance to let go of those feelings. If you sensed this, were these feelings connected to some ideas of yourself as virtuous or martyred? Try again until you can feel yourself become more comfortable with the idea of being free of the pain of neurotic guilt.

Perhaps you kept having the idea as you were trying to work with a particularly strong guilt memory that you should be punished. If so, could you imagine creating a punishment by which you could learn something without being self-destructive? This is not a highly recommended way of managing guilt, but it is good for people who feel stuck with the idea of self-punishment as an answer to relieving guilt.

What about the idea of seeking forgiveness from the

other person and from yourself? Can you let yourself take this action rather than get stuck with your guilt? Let yourself relax again and fantasize plans of making amends until you find you have created one which seems right to you. If the other person is unavailable, imagine having a dialogue with that person. Try to see yourself from the other person's point of view and allow that person to forgive you. In my experience with clients, I find that the forgiveness comes automatically from the "other" person imagined in the dialogue and great relief usually follows. Perhaps forgiveness of yourself can follow out of a sense of love for yourself as a human being who must make mistakes in order to maintain membership in the species.

Another effective method for reducing people's guilt and concomitant obsessive worries is the use of a special time set aside for feeling guilty. You will probably have to try this to believe it works since it may sound strange. The idea is to sit down alone without distractions or interruptions for one half-hour morning and night and do nothing but feel guilty. This must be practiced regularly to work. Both guilts and punishments should be thought of as you usually do and then in an exaggerated form. For instance, if you think of a window you broke as a child and denied doing this, you may feel that you should be scolded by your mother even today for that. Exaggerated, you may want to imagine being written out of her will or hanged for breaking that window and lying. If you decide to do this exercise, it is important to stay with the guilt and punishment the entire half-hour and practice without fail. Follow your own sense of when it is all right to stop this program of reducing neurotic guilt.

Preventing further build-up of guilt is very important. Assertiveness suggestions such as those mentioned earlier in this chapter and in other books and courses can help you learn to release yourself from feeling that you must please others. Assertiveness can also help you learn to say a guilt-free "no" to some of the demands on you from others. This prevents an automatic guilt response if you decide that responding to a demand is too draining or just not desirable.

Anxiety Anxiety is a major experiential component of a stress reaction. It is a feeling of apprehension and dread. In some instances, as when facing a rattlesnake, this feeling may be realistic or objective and is then best labeled as fear. Anxiety with no clear external cause or which is much stronger than the situation warrants is known as neurotic anxiety. This kind of anxiety is maladaptive since it is a false alarm that sends the body into a stress reaction for no useful purpose. Neurotic anxiety can be a chronic, rather general experience of life called trait anxiety or it can be a transitory emotional state called state anxiety. People usually express great relief at being rid of both kinds.

Awareness of anxiety can be blocked by many mental defense mechanisms such as denial, repression, projection, and rationalization. We are at our healthiest when we do not need defense mechanisms to cope with our anxiety but can be aware of it and discharge it in a harmless manner.

In Chapter Four you identified your bodily signs of anxiety and general stress. Typically, tachycardia, respiratory disturbances, tremors, perspiration, nausea, muscle tension, lightheadedness, and restlessness are present to some degree in any anxiety reaction. Paying attention to your mental/emotional state will also reveal signs of anxiety. It can also be identified by noticing cognitive predictions of tragedy and doom. This may happen in visual form, daydreaming, or thought. If you observe yourself closely, you may find that you image or think of rather catastrophic events without full and clear awareness of these. For instance, on the way to work you may experience several "flashes" of an angry scene between yourself and Doctor X and become anxious without noticing the cause of it because you are busy driving your car. Again, then, deliberately paying more attention to your own experience is the important first step in regulating your level of stress. If you let yourself be aware of even the mildest forms of anxiety, it is then possible to cope with this form of distress without resorting totally to defense mechanisms.

Once aware of anxiety, what are some effective ways to cope with it on a mental/emotional level? First, remember that our bodies and minds are intimately related, so using the physical relaxation response methods discussed in Chapter Four will help lower your level of anxiety perceived physically. In fact, such things as biofeedback, deep muscle relaxation, and other methods of eliciting a relaxation response are usually among the most successful methods for reducing the somatic aspects of anxiety.

Highly important to the process of reducing anxiety is remembering to breathe. Often when we are tense our muscles are tight and we tend to hold our breath. This creates more tension which creates more breath-holding and so forth. Yawning and sighing may be signs that we have not been breathing deeply enough. Practicing the "mini-relaxation response" as described earlier helps people learn to change their habits of breathing and avoid breath-holding.

When people are anxious, I often recommend a breath-counting meditation since this helps them focus on both their breathing and on the neutral repetitive task of counting, which replaces anxious thoughts. The meditation is conducted as follows:

Sit in a position comfortable enough that you can relax your muscles and breathe easily. Take a deep, relaxing breath, allowing your abdominal muscles to expand as you inhale through your nose. Then exhale and let your tension go and begin simply noticing your breathing without attempting to control it. Just breathe naturally through your nose, simply letting the air come in slowly—allowing the air to come in and go out at its own rate. As you exhale slowly, mentally count "one" and as you slowly inhale, think the word "and." As you exhale again, mentally count "two" and as you inhale think to yourself the word "and." As you exhale, count "three" and on the inhale think "and." As you exhale again, count "four" and on the inhale the word 'and." When you have finished with the fourth exhale, begin counting with "one" again so that you can keep this very simple and not wonder later if you were at twenty-seven or twenty-nine. As you get more relaxed and deeper into a meditative state, you may forget at some point which number you were thinking as you exhaled. No problem. Whenever in doubt, simply count the next exhale as "one" and proceed from there. At times this meditation allays anxiety and at other times it helps to focus and clarify the anxiety. Either of these two states is preferable to most people than simply experiencing the full force of the anxiety. If your anxiety becomes more clear to you, simply observe it and see what you can learn from it. When you feel sufficiently calm and wish to return to a wakeful state, just be very gentle with yourself, open your eyes, and sit quietly for a moment before becoming active again.

A third possibility for coping with anxiety is that of creating a private, safe, mental environment that can be used as a calming retreat place during anxious periods to gain perspective and peace of mind. This beautiful, imagined "place" can be conjured up just prior to practicing any relaxation or meditative method or can be brought to mind as part of a brief relaxation process any time during the day or can be "flashed to" during a period of uncomfortably high anxiety. To create your own mental/emotional retreat center, read the suggestions below carefully and then sit for a few minutes to give yourself a chance to follow these directions and create your own special environment.

First, be sure you are seated comfortably and take a deep, relaxing, abdominal breath. As you relax, let yourself begin to imagine a general setting in which you will create your own very special, private place of relaxation. This may be a setting of which you have memories, such as the mountains or the shore, or you may find that you quickly choose a beautiful environment that seems new to you. Just be sure that this general setting is the most beautiful, calming, and peaceful setting you can imagine. Now let yourself delineate in your mind's eye some boundaries around this setting within which you will create a structure of some sort to provide you with peace and relaxation. Let yourself visualize the dimensions of this structure. Then begin to build the structure, choosing your building materials carefully so that you are creating the most beautiful structure you have ever seen. Let yourself choose colors for your shelter that are stress-reducing and comforting. Notice what kind of light you would like to have in this space and allow that light to be there. Also add any sounds you find particularly soothing, as well as any aromas or fragrances you might find appealing. Notice the textures you have chosen. See if these are smooth or rough, and create them as you want them to be. Now imagine yourself inside this structure. Notice the size of yourself and the size of the structure and adjust these sizes until their ratio is comfortable. Then notice what position your body is in and see it being very relaxed. See your face looking relaxed and your breathing being slow and deep and regular. Notice what kind of clothing you are wearing as you relax and feel calm within your new structure. Now notice an easy route of entry and exit from your space to your everyday life. See yourself being able to move easily in and out of this newly-created mental/emotional retreat. Remind yourself that this is a place not only to gain a respite from anxiety, but to gain perspective and clarity on your anxiety as well.

If you decide to use this imagery of a retreat place, you may find that its characteristics change over time. It is likely to become increasingly calming also.

A fourth way of coping with anxiety is specifically for cognitive anxiety—that sense of apprehension and "speed up" which can be very uncomfortable. This particular kind of meditation is a concentrative type, which restricts outer awareness and reduces reactivity to environmental stimuli. A concentrative meditation involves the use of a word or words or an object to focus one's attention upon to the exclusion of other stimuli such as one's own anxious thoughts. This particular type of meditation involves the use of a mantra, since this seems to help people focus their attention when they are anxious. A mantra is a word or phrase or sound either actually said or thought with each exhale. Benson in *The Relaxation Response*[22] suggests the use of the word "one." There are also many possible ancient mantras from Eastern religions. I usually suggest that a person "find" his or her own mantra by sitting quietly and allowing oneself to utter sounds, one at a time, until a sound that feels calming or comforting or pleasant in some way is found. It is best that this sound does not elicit many associations since it is meant simply as an anchor point for the mind during meditation. Try this process and see what sound you find that is right for you.

To use your mantra as a meditative tool, sit quietly where you will not be interrupted, take a deep relaxing breath, close your eyes, and either whisper or think your mantra each time you exhale. After you are in a rhythm of doing this, you may notice that your mind drifts to various thoughts. In most cases you will want to gently pull your mind back to concentrating on your mantra as you exhale. However, you may decide at times that you want to stay with a certain thought or stream of thought, especially if these thoughts clarify your anxiety or help in some other way to resolve it. Occasionally, when the anxiety is clarified, people feel that the meditation is "making" them anxious. There are limits, of course, but people usually find it ultimately rewarding to stay with the experience of their own anxiety as if they are noticing it from some distance and accepting it as part of the meditative process. Part of the reason this type of meditation experience is helpful stems from the fact that anxiety-provoking images and thoughts are experienced while in a relaxed state so that a global desensitization process is possible.

Another effective method of coping with anxiety is

systematic desensitization. We discussed the use of this process for dealing with fears. You may want to review that section for a moment right now. Anxieties can be controlled using the same methodology. A hierarchy is constructed which has to do with a single strong anxiety, containing sentences that describe the least anxiety-provoking to the most anxiety-provoking images. Deep relaxation is practiced before, during, and after imagining each description in the hierarchy. It is important to work very thoroughly and slowly on this process.

Both meditation and systematic desensitization help manage symptoms of anxiety and help prevent anxiety responses. Changing one's cognitive behavior also helps reduce anxiety and is a very important way to prevent anxiety through changing the very thought processes that create the anxiety. Most of our anxieties are triggered by incessant worry about others' opinions of us, or their anger toward us, or losing their love. We also make ourselves anxious by assuming that some event in the future is going to be horrible or unbearable in some way. A good format for combating these irrational thoughts is Burns' double-column technique as noted previously in this chapter. Turn back to Figure 3, and use this structure to help you become aware of some of your typical anxious thoughts. Write these in the first column. In the second column write a rebuttal thought which is rational and peace-inducing. Drill yourself on these thoughts and their rebuttals for a few minutes each day until you find that you are beginning to automatically correct your anxiety-provoking thoughts as they occur.

Depression   Stressful events such as losses, particularly of love relationships, can trigger off both sadness and depression. Sadness is felt over a loss and is normal, but depression is felt over a loss when a person is sad and has declared him or herself a "loser" in some sense. Depression can be experienced as a dark heavy gloom which hides reasons to continue living. Life seems to hold no excitement or fun. Sleep is disturbed; appetite for food and sex may be lost. Depression can also be hidden in somatic disorders, pain, irritability, and lethargy. Some depressions are biochemically induced, but most are a result of negative images and thoughts about oneself. For instance, a person adds to the misery of losing a lover by relentlessly pelting him or herself with accusatory questions such as "Am I capable of loving another person?" and "Am I attractive and worthy of another's love?" There is also the typical torture of thinking that the person just lost was "the only one in the world I could ever be that close to." Very deep sadness naturally occurs when the loss is particularly traumatic and real, such as a sudden, unexpected death of a loved one, permanent loss of one's own physical abilities, being diagnosed as terminally ill, and total financial collapse. Even these losses do not have to lead to a chronic depressive state in which the person is feeling down on him or herself in some way.

Following is the Beck Depression Inventory.[23] Take a few minutes to circle the number in each of these items which applies to you at present.

Beck Depression Inventory *   Table A.

1. 0   I do not feel sad.
   1   I feel sad.
   2   I am sad all the time and I can't snap out of it.
   3   I am so sad or unhappy that I can't stand it.

2. 0 I am not particularly discouraged about the future.
   1 I feel discouraged about the future.
   2 I feel I have nothing to look forward to.
   3 I feel that the future is hopeless and that things cannot improve.

3. 0 I do not feel like a failure.
   1 I feel I have failed more than the average person.
   2 As I look back on my life, all I can see is a lot of failures.
   3 I feel I am a complete failure as a person.

4. 0 I get as much satisfaction out of things as I used to.
   1 I don't enjoy things the way I used to.
   2 I don't get real satisfaction out of anything anymore.
   3 I am dissatisfied or bored with everything.

5. 0 I don't feel particularly guilty.
   1 I feel guilty a good part of the time.
   2 I feel quite guilty most of the time.
   3 I feel guilty all of the time.

6. 0 I don't feel I am being punished.
   1 I feel I may be punished.
   2 I expect to be punished.
   3 I feel I am being punished.

7. 0 I don't feel disappointed in myself.
   1 I am disappointed in myself.
   2 I am disgusted with myself.
   3 I hate myself.

8. 0 I don't feel I am any worse than anybody else.
   1 I am critical of myself for my weaknesses or mistakes.
   2 I blame myself all the time for my faults.
   3 I blame myself for everything bad that happens.

9. 0 I don't have any thoughts of killing myself.
   1 I have thoughts of killing myself, but I would not carry them out.
   2 I would like to kill myself.
   3 I would kill myself if I had the chance.

10. 0 I don't cry any more than usual.
    1 I cry more now than I used to.
    2 I cry all the time now.

    3   I used to be able to cry, but now I can't cry even though I want to.

11. 0   I am no more irritated by things than I ever am.
      1   I am slightly more irritated now than usual.
      2   I am quite annoyed or irritated a good deal of the time.
      3   I feel irritated all the time now.

12. 0   I have not lost interest in other people.
      1   I am less interested in other people than I used to be.
      2   I have lost most of my interest in other people.
      3   I have lost all of my interest in other people.

13. 0   I make decisions about as well as I ever could.
      1   I put off making decisions more than I used to.
      2   I have greater difficulty in making decisions than before.
      3   I can't make decisions at all anymore.

14. 0   I don't feel that I look any worse than I used to.
      1   I am worried that I am looking old or unattractive.
      2   I feel that there are permanent changes in my appearance that make me look unattractive.
      3   I believe that I look ugly.

15. 0   I can work about as well as before.
      1   It takes an extra effort to get started at doing something.
      2   I have to push myself very hard to do anything.
      3   I can't do any work at all.

16. 0   I can sleep as well as usual.
      1   I don't sleep as well as I used to.
      2   I wake up 1-2 hours earlier than usual and find it hard to get back to sleep.
      3   I wake up several hours earlier than I used to and cannot get back to sleep.

17. 0   I don't get more tired than usual.
      1   I get tired more easily than I used to.
      2   I get tired from doing almost anything.
      3   I am too tired to do anything.

18. 0   My appetite is no worse than usual.
      1   My appetite is not as good as it used to be.
      2   My appetite is much worse now.
      3   I have no appetite at all anymore.

19. 0   I haven't lost much weight, if any, lately.
    1   I have lost more than five pounds.
    2   I have lost more than ten pounds.
    3   I have lost more than fifteen pounds.

20. 0   I am no more worried about my health than usual.
    1   I am worried about physical problems such as aches and pains, or upset stomach, or constipation.
    2   I am very worried about physical problems and it's hard to think of much else.
    3   I am so worried about my physical problems that I cannot think about anything else.

21. 0   I have not noticed any recent change in my interest in sex.
    1   I am less interested in sex than I used to be.
    2   I am much less interested in sex now.
    3   I have lost interest in sex completely.

Interpreting the Beck Depression Inventory   Now that you have completed the test, add up the score for each of the twenty-one questions and obtain the total. Since the highest score that you can get on each of the twenty-one questions is three, the highest possible total for the whole test would be sixty-three (this would mean you circled number three on all twenty-one questions). Since the lowest score for each question is zero, the lowest possible score for the test would be zero (this would mean you circled zero on each question).

You can now evaluate your depression according to Table B.

Table B. Interpreting the Beck Depression Inventory

Total Score	*Levels of Depression* *
1–10	These ups and downs are considered normal.

11–16	Mild mood disturbance.
17–20	Borderline clinical depression.
21–30	Moderate depression.
31–40	Severe depression.
over 40	Extreme depression.

*A persistent score of 17 or above indicates you may need professional treatment.

Now that you have completed the inventory, total your score and use Table B as a way to evaluate the level of your depression. As you can see, a persistent score of 17 or more indicates a need for professional assistance in Beck's opinion. In that case, the following suggestions may be helpful, but should not be used as a substitute for professional help.

Beck[24] has also suggested some attitudes people carry with them which predispose them to excessive sadness or depression. Examples are:

- In order to be happy, I have to be successful at whatever I undertake.
- To be happy, I must be accepted by all people at all times.
- If I make a mistake, it means that I'm inept.
- I can't live without love.
- If somebody disagrees with me, it means he doesn't like me.
- My value as a person depends on what others think of me.[25]

Are you aware of carrying around any of these attitudes? Take a moment to make two columns on a paper and list your own attitudes which may be similar in nature to Beck's examples. Now make a rational rebuttal statement to each of these attitudes and jot these in the right-hand column. When you find yourself thinking an irrational, depressing thought, try stopping that thought and replacing it with a rational, self-enhancing statement.

Let's go through an example of healthy grieving of a loss and see some of the pitfalls which could lead to depression. In my practice I see many professional women who are clinically depressed by the loss of a love relationship. Perhaps you can recall your last loss of a person important to you and imagine going through that loss again as we outline the coping process.

In the beginning is the importance of defining what you have actually lost. Try to be very specific and separate "real" losses (such as missing eating meals together) from irrational ones (those that are formulated as "he was the *only* person in the world who will ever . . .").

When you feel like crying, do so with gusto. Sobbing is much more healing than sniffling and daintily tearing. The process of vigorously sobbing and wailing can lead to great relief. A few days off from your usual life style to cry and talk can help speed this initial stage of grieving.

As times goes on, what I call "titering" becomes important. This means allowing yourself to go ahead and feel the sadness when a "wave" of grief hits, or, if there are no automatic waves, allowing time to be quiet and let the sadness come to the surface so that you can discharge it by crying and talking about it. The titering concept describes the process of allowing as much sadness into your awareness as possible without immobilizing yourself. As life goes on it will be business as usual at times with demands upon you from others. It is very important during this phase to take good care of yourself physically by making sure you are exercising whether you want to or not, eating well or taking vitamin and mineral supplements at least, and pampering yourself with warm baths, favorite snacks, and by accepting the attention and comfort others are offering you. Many of my clients have found this a particularly fine time to take advantage of some massage therapy to help reduce muscle tension, let out feelings, and feel comforted by being touched. It is also a good time to use a relaxation tape since this, too, helps in reducing tension and supporting the fullest expression of feelings.

Along the way it is important to watch for irrational elements of the grieving process, which could turn your emotional state to depression. The double-column method is very helpful for this purpose if done each day. The automatic thoughts may be depressing. The rational statements of rebuttal can counter the depressing thoughts. They can also be utilized as affirmative self-statements, which can be said to oneself over and over during the day.

Another part of healthily proceeding through the grieving process without getting depressed is closely observing the imagery you create. Do you "see" yourself, for instance, being lonely and unloved the rest of your life? It is important to be aware of and correct these powerful negative images and substitute positive ones. Let yourself create images for yourself of a happy, rewarding future. Choose specific times in the weeks, months, and even years ahead and see yourself enjoying life at these points.

Nurses are often exposed to repetitive losses which may seem minor or, at least, not tragic each time, but may accumulate and cause problems. For example, we "lose" clients when they are discharged from the hospital just as they are getting well and might be more rewarding to be with. We also "lose" clients we may not have seen in a conscious state when they die in the emergency room, or we may "lose" clients we know and love when they die after a long illness. Our stress levels can benefit greatly by our ability to stay aware of these constant losses and let ourselves grieve as necessary to help prevent a chronically sad or depressed state.

The next section of the study of self-regulation of emotional responses will attend to troublesome mental/emotional states composed of many of the feelings just discussed. Theoretically, if we managed our negative feelings well we would not suffer with any of the combination states. Since perfectionism, insomnia, loneliness, addictive behavior, and sexual problems are common results of stress as well as being stressors themselves, I will at least briefly address these problem areas.

Perfectionism   This troublesome mental/emotional pattern can contain almost all the negative feelings discussed so far. People can be anxious about and afraid of making a mistake, feel guilty and angry if they do, and eventually feel depressed when perfection does not manifest itself often enough in their lives. Perfectionism is a compulsion to "do it just exactly right" and is obviously a highly stressful behavior pattern. It is hard on the body, too, since people tend to be very tense while waiting to make a mistake or catch someone else making one.

Think about the degree of your own perfectionism. Do you like things to go "just right"? Do you get notably upset when you make a mistake? Do you watch others and notice their flaws? Do you wish you could get them to do better? Do you notice your mistakes more quickly than your correct moves?

A Gestalt therapy method I often use with clients to help them become aware of parts of themselves is to imagine the part that is, in pure form, their perfectionist. Sit back and let yourself visualize the part of you that is nearly always alert to mistakes and dangers of failing in some way. Let yourself get clear on what that part's lines are to your "main" self. Recently a client was doing this and imagined her mother sitting on her shoulder like a small ghost who could whisper in her ear all day things like, "Now watch out—you almost said the wrong thing to that Congressman" and "If you write the wrong words in this memo, many people will lose faith in you." This client learned to talk and think back to her perfectionistic self as personified in the form of the tiny mother ghost. She was eventually able to win battles with the ghost, and at times did not give in to the demands for perfection but tolerated her fear and anxiety instead as she refused to double- and triple-check on her own actions. Do the same with your perfectionistic part, whatever age or size it may seem. Let yourself carry on a subtle dialogue with the troublesome, nagging part until it is under your control.

Another way to lessen perfectionism is to write a "thank you and goodbye letter" to perfectionism as if it were a person who has been with you for some time. In this letter, Ms. Perfectionism is thanked for all the assistance she has given you and is told to move along now since you are confident you can live much more happily without her. Be very detailed in thanking her and in listing the reasons you will do better without her. If you are inclined toward enacting scenes, it may be helpful to read your letter aloud as if directed to Ms. Perfectionism, or read it to your mate or close friend to reinforce the power of your words.

Imagery can also be helpful in combating perfectionism. Try relaxing and seeing yourself doing less than a perfect job at some task. What happens? How do you feel? Keep imagining this until the choices of "I get fired or divorced or murdered" drop out and more realistic outcomes emerge. Another imagery exercise involves letting yourself visualize scene after scene of yourself deliberately making outrageous mistakes—let this turn into a slapstick comedy and enjoy your own laughter.

Insomnia Millions of people agonize over their perception that they cannot get to sleep or stay asleep or do not feel rested when they awake. Sleep disorders can be caused by one or more of a wide variety of problems including jet lag, preoccupation with the day's events, pain, and drug withdrawal. Many disease processes can cause some form of insomnia. An underlying or obvious depression can also do this. Circadian rhythms, often influenced by stressors, are very important factors in insomnia. Nurses who work various shifts are all too familiar with insomnia resulting from disturbance of the circadian rhythms. Insomnia is one of the better examples of a condition which often results from unmanaged distress and then becomes, by its nature, a stressor in itself, causing more insomnia. Besides lying awake from worry about not getting enough sleep, people also tend to worry about their ability to mentally, emotionally, and physically perform well the next day. The use of drugs to induce and maintain sleep has not provided a satisfactory answer for insomnia except in treating acute situational disturbances in sleep. For the person with chronic insomnia, accommodation to increasingly higher doses may take place, leaving the person with the problem of withdrawal, which in itself causes insomnia.

When I see people in my classes or clinical practice who complain of insomnia, we do an evaluation together to see what factors seem responsible for the insomnia and begin a program designed to eliminate these factors or perceive them differently. Since insomnia can be a very disturbing and disruptive experience, we may elect to use some behavioral therapy and relaxation therapy to achieve a better sleep pattern while the underlying causes are being dealt with. The remainder of this section will focus on behavioral strategies for inducing sleep.

First is physical relaxation. Many people report being able to sleep much better or having no more trouble with insomnia simply by practicing the "Suggestions for General Relaxation" tape[26] two to six times a day until they learn to stay in a more physically and mentally relaxed state.

Second is relaxing the mind. Attitudes toward insomnia are very important. It is easy to build up a great deal of anxiety about not sleeping. The more a person can develop a detached attitude—one in which you feel as if it does not matter whether you go to sleep or not—the more likely you are to fall asleep. Developing a detached attitude about disturbing events of the day or chronic conflicts can also help reduce distressing mental activity. Meditation can also contribute to the relaxation of your mind. Practicing meditation regularly each day can have a general mentally relaxing effect and help decrease insomnia. The use of breathing and counting meditations to induce sleep may also be helpful. For instance, the breath-counting meditation described earlier is an effective method as is the age-old process of counting sheep. Also any constant and repetitive mental task can help move you toward a sleep state. Perhaps we fall asleep out of self-defense against boredom with these methods! Some people prefer to use a hypnotic tape such as "Suggestions for Restful Sleep,"[27] since they can maintain a more passive and relaxed attitude while hearing someone else speak slowly, softly, and rhythmically. This tape and others like it are designed for use when you are feeling somewhat inclined toward sleep but want the inclination enhanced.

Decreasing use of stimulants or cutting them out of one's diet altogether may be very helpful in reducing the incidence of insomnia.

Vigorous exercise several hours prior to sleep can first be stimulating but then relaxing, since the muscles have relaxed and physical energy and "nervous energy" have been expended.

Creating a cool, quiet, restful space and utilizing it well are very important. Most people prefer a room which allows humidity control and also control over the amount of sunlight that can enter. If you tend to utilize your bed for sleeping, sexual activity, communications center, snack bar, worrying place, and TV room, you may be setting yourself up for insomnia. Using your bed for sleeping and making love can help you train yourself to expect relaxation and sleep when in your bed.

Maintaining a fairly regular schedule of waking and sleeping and other activities can be helpful in promoting restful sleep. Particularly important is a regular schedule of sleeping. This involves getting up at approximately the same time each day and not allowing yourself to oversleep or nap during the day. The exception to this is avoiding going to bed when not sleepy. It is advisable to stay up reading, being involved in a quiet hobby, or watching TV until you are sleepy. A consistent nightly ritual can help you train yourself to fall asleep. This ritual may include such things as reading something light, taking a warm bath, and practicing some meditation or using the time for quiet inspiration and prayer.

Many people include in their sleep-inducing ritual some kind of natural sedative such as L-tryptophan, apparently the ingredient our grandmothers knew about in warm milk and chamomile tea.

Recently, Czeisler and associates[28] reported that sleep is highly correlated with the body temperature part of circadian rhythms. According to this research, the normal time to fall asleep is when the body's temperature is near its daily low. The normal waking time is correlated with the body's close approach to its daily temperature high. Czeisler and Weitzman at Montefiore have used their research results to formulate treatment programs for those with sleep onset insomnia. The treatment involves helping people shift their temperature rhythm. The results of their treatment program are encouraging for shift workers and jet setters alike.

Loneliness   We have all experienced the distress of loneliness in at least one of its many forms. Loneliness is a feeling of being disconnected, cut off from others, or a longing for someone to connect with. It can easily be transformed into feelings of being forgotten, ignored, unwanted, and unloved, which then can further change to a sense of oneself as unlovable and unworthy of the attention of others. Loneliness and other stressful mental/emotional states, such as depression, anger, fear, and guilt, are not unknown to one another.

Both understimulation and overstimulation can lead to loneliness. You may have experienced loneliness at a crowded cocktail party or professional meeting if you sensed you were not being understood or accepted. On the other hand, I have talked with many nurses from small cities or rural areas around the country who are interested in holistic health philosophy and practice, but who feel a strong sense of the "Lone Ranger Syndrome" because they have no peers with similar interests in their area. Loneliness can be situational or characterological. Situational loneliness results from the loss of a relationship or familiar surroundings while characterological loneliness involves the subjective experience of loneliness no matter what the circumstances. If this form is constantly bothersome, it deserves professional attention. Fear of rejection, lack of confidence and self-esteem, and fear of too close an involvement with another are common problems of lonely people.

Since most of us find loneliness so unpleasant, we avoid it by keeping busy and in that process may starve ourselves of stress-reducing and revitalizing time alone. One way of handling loneliness, in fact, is to spend quiet, relaxing, enjoyable time alone to desensitize yourself to the fear of being alone. Treating yourself well and doing some activities alone can help build a sense of self-respect and independence to hedge against the notion that you have to depend on others for happiness and contentment.

Thinking clearly also helps loneliness dissipate. First is realizing the difference between *wanting* and *needing* certain kinds of connections with others. Thinking in terms of *needing* others as one needs air and water can be dangerous if it leads to unmet expectations and disappointments. Thinking that you want certain connections and that it is unfortunate not to have them at this moment is a less desperation-producing thought than that you must have certain relationships or else. Being clear about your wants helps put them in perspective and allows hope without potential disaster if wants do not materialize quickly or at all.

Another helpful way to manage feelings of loneliness is to accept responsibility for these feelings and control over them so you can take remedial action. Pushing through your resistances to initiating contacts with others is part of this way of thinking. Talking with others in a present-oriented, self-disclosing manner is usually a step toward feeling connected and less lonely.

Drawing a mental line between "I am alone tonight" and "I am unlovable" is of critical importance. Reminding yourself when lonely of your better qualities is one way to stay rational and avoid hysteria and self-pity.

Many people find a basic answer to loneliness in spiritual studies and development. Meditation and prayer can be powerful experiences of belonging or fitting into a natural scheme of things.

Addictive Behavior   Several volumes could be dedicated to the etiology and treatment of addictive behavior, the habitual and compulsive use of some substance, such as food, caffeine, nicotine, alcohol, or other drugs. Use of these substances in an uncontrolled way is usually aimed toward a relaxed or at least less stressful state of being.

We will discuss addictive behavior generally in this section since the behavior is similar whether the object is candy or alcohol. Underlying psychodynamics vary with the target substance and intensity of the addiction, but may not be necessary to realize before one is able to stop the behavior.

The first hurdle is breaking through the mental defense of denial. This is particularly true for people who are dependent on alcohol or other drugs. "I can stop any time I want to" is a common defense. Let yourself think of a possible addiction of your own. Do you have negative feelings toward that very idea? Perhaps you actually do not have an addiction in the strictest sense, but even so you may want to be open to the possibility.

Let yourself think of some substance you rely on to help you cope with stressors and use it as your example in the following discussion of controlling addictive behavior.

First is collecting data on when you want the substance, where you are when you want it, what thoughts you think at the time of wanting it, what feelings you have at this time, and what bodily sensations you have at this time. Keep a record in a small portable notebook on these events. Just letting yourself be acutely aware of these factors for one 24-hour period can be of great help in revealing cues to assist you in learning to manage the drive to take the substance.

Next, let yourself be creative in designing other options for yourself once you are aware of a cue indicating that the addictive drive has just been triggered. For example, instead of opening the refrigerator door to reach for food or a beer, you could have a list of options which might include doing a very brief relaxation exercise, calling a friend, or thinking of some pleasant event you have planned in the future. The point is to try various options. Think of these as experimental and time-limited so that you are not tied to any commitment to stop the addictive behavior too suddenly or too stringently. Be sure to reward yourself in some way each time you are able to use an option to the addictive behavior. If possible, get part or all of your social network involved in rewarding you for controlling your addictive impulses.

Assertiveness training is often a valuable help in overcoming addictive patterning since it aids in learning to actively get what you want rather than passively substituting a substance for satisfaction. Self-help and therapy groups focused on particular addictive patterns, such as Alcoholics Anonymous or Overeaters Anonymous, can also be of great support and guidance when mutual problems and goals are discussed.

I often make personalized relaxation and imagery tapes for clients with addictive problems. You may want to make one of these for yourself. A good length is from ten to twenty minutes. Start with some of your favorite suggestions for relaxation, then continue with suggestions of thoughts and images relating to claiming control over the impulses and gaining freedom from them. For example:

I am relaxed and in control of my emotions.
Each day I am becoming less dependent on _____.
I feel satisfied without _____.
I see myself as free from _____.
I am happy without _____.
Every day I am more relaxed and free from _____.
I am proud of myself for being free from _____.

At the end you may want to include a suggestion to visualize yourself in whatever way you would like to be, perhaps a nonsmoker or a thin person. Then suggest coming back to a wakeful state, rested and more free of the addictive substance. Practice this series of suggestions two to six times each day, both when you feel your addictive drive and at times when you do not experience it.

Sexual Dysfunctions Like other stressful maladies, sexual dysfunctions can be complex blends of such things as unfortunate early life experiences, an unfulfilling relationship with a sexual partner, and self-defeating behavior, thought, and emotional patterns. Some common dysfunctions are premature ejaculation, vaginismus, inhibited sexual excitement, and inhibited orgasm. These conditions can improve by practicing effective methods of managing life's distress in general since they often have to do with a high anxiety level.

If you believe you are in some way sexually dysfunctional and this is bothersome to you, it is wise to seek professional guidance. If you feel that your sexual experiences are not particularly stressful and are not chronically problematic, you may want to try some of the following approaches with enrichment in mind.

In a very general way, what seems to help with sexual dysfunction problems is relaxing, desensitizing to specific sexual situations, and allowing more enjoyment of sensory stimulation. Relaxation can be accomplished by various methods already presented, such as biofeedback relaxation tapes, and meditative methods. Changing your attitudes toward your own sexuality may be helpful if you learned to feel anxiety, fear, or guilt about sexual feelings or behaviors. The double-column, rational thinking approach mentioned earlier in this chapter can be helpful in alleviating these feelings.

Also helpful in reducing anxiety is the process of desensitization originally developed by Masters and Johnson.[29] Basically, this involves systematically progressing from low anxiety-arousal sexual behavior to high anxiety-arousal behavior slowly enough to allow comfort, pleasure, and new sexual skills to develop between partners. This desensitization can be done with imagery as well by first visualizing a very relaxing, pleasant scene, relaxing your body, and then imaging a sexual scene of low anxiety-arousal. Repeat the process by imaging a relaxed scene and then sexual scenes of progressively greater anxiety. This alternating is done until the specific anxiety-producing scenes no longer elicit anxiety.

Another way of utilizing relaxation and imagery is to visually create scenes of yourself enjoying sexual pleasure. Allowing this kind of relaxation, especially in a vivid step-by-step rehearsal, helps guide behavior when one is in the actual situation.

Using Knowledge and Experience to Regulate Stressors

We have seen how important regulating our beliefs and our emotional responses can be as ways of effectively managing stressors in our lives. Using the knowledge and experience we have and gaining even more knowledge and experience are often overlooked as methods of stress management. Sometimes it is obvious that our knowledge does not help us effectively manage stress. One example of this is a radiologist or oncological nurse who smokes two packs of cigarettes a day. Usually, at least, our knowledge and experience does us no harm, and it sometimes proves crucial in our ability to handle stressors.

Everyone has a certain level of expertise at decision-making, goal setting, and time management. Let's look at these again, however, in terms of adding to your knowledge and changing some of your behavior in these three areas so that your ability to manage stressors is enhanced.

Decision Making   Feeling "stuck" between two (or more) alternatives can be very distressing, especially if feeling stuck is a way of life. Often, unresolved fears will play a part in experiencing ambivalence—fear of making a mistake, hurting or angering someone, or losing face or money. You may also be familiar with the immobility in decision-making that can prevail when a "I know on an intellectual level what to do, but my gut says . . . " situation exists.

To get off dead center, making a decision and acting on it can allow relief and healing of stress symptoms.

These positive results vary according to the conscious and unconscious pressure felt from having been stuck.

One way to go on through the decision-making process is to determine what more, if any, information you want and get it. Remind yourself that most decisions can be made quickly without agonizing. Separate fantasied disastrous outcomes from rational predictions of outcomes, i.e., will you *really* lose your job if you decide to take a stand on issue X? Again, assertiveness training can be helpful in becoming less fearful of taking a position on an issue and defending that position.

The old two-column trick of writing the advantages of a decision in one column and the disadvantages in another column is useful to many people who have had extended internal duels over a decision. Another method of finalizing a decision is to sit quietly with your eyes closed and imagine two characters debating the issue. These characters can be two cartoon characters, animals, or whatever comes to mind which can play out clearly the opposing sides of yourself on the issue. Doing this from a quieted state of mind seems to allow a resolution more quickly than thinking it through with your eyes open.

Goal Setting   In speaking of setting goals as a way to manage stress, we can include a whole range of goals from those for work today to family-oriented goals in years to come, to economic and career goals. Setting clear goals can give direction to our energy. They are statements of what we want. This is different than having expectations that goals must be attained or we have failed.

Take a few minutes to retrieve the list of goals you made earlier in this chapter and add to it now. Be specific about your goals. For instance, rather than writing "learning more," write exactly what you want to learn and by when. Keep these goals realistic, that is, to things you really are willing to work for and that would actually be good for you. Write both short- and long-term goals and specify times by which you want to have attained these goals.

Now prioritize your goals. Choose a few of the most important ones and keep them available so that you see them each day. Ask yourself occasionally during the week if you are conducting your life in a way that is compatible with your stated goals. You may want to revise your goals or at least their priority occasionally since it is natural that these will change.

Time Management   You will recall that one of the Type A hallmarks is a chronic sense of urgency about time. How did you fare on the time management questionnaire on page 182? Does it seem to you that you never have enough time to do all you want to do in a day? This constant sense of your life being too crowded can have insidiously stressful effects, as can swinging abruptly among periods of frantic activity, procrastination, and rest.

How we conceptualize time is crucial to how we manage it. Are you driven toward certain goals as if sure death awaits you in three days and all must be accomplished by then? Or do you have an attitude that nothing is very important and wind up procrastinating? The issue of the personal meaning of time relates closely to your short- and long-term goals. Perhaps you could take a moment to review your goals now in light of the influence on how you use time. Do the goals lead to feeling time-pressured or can you imagine yourself achieving them at a comfortable pace?

The question of how to manage time at work and at

home so that effectiveness is maintained and our stress kept at a reasonable level is worth considering in some detail in view of the distress potential inherent in poor management of time. Following are some basic principles and suggestions for effective time management.

The first part of solving any time management problem is to collect data on how your time is typically used. Try this for three 24-hour periods, using a coding system so that the logging itself will not take significant time. Be as detailed as you can so that you can easily identify areas of time waste in the day (as differentiated from free time or time to relax). Note from your log your favorite, least favorite, most relaxing, and most stressful ways of using your time. Are there areas of the log representing ineffective use of time, i.e., use that is not your best choice or is not worth it in terms of results?

Planning the use of time is a key factor in effectively utilizing time. Many of us let ourselves feel so rushed that we are irritated by the idea of planning because we perceive no time to use for this. It is undeniable, however, that both short- and long-range planning helps us reduce stress. Unplanned time often leads to adopting a crisis mentality in which we occupy ourselves by responding to urgency rather than the actual importance of a task.

A stress-reducing habit to get into is writing out a brief "to do" list at the beginning of each day's activities. Prioritize these in order of importance, taking urgency into consideration. Schedule some time for long-range planning, routine tasks, and breaks. Pacing yourself is significant here. Pay attention to your body rhythms so that you are handling the most challenging or important tasks at your prime time of the day. Follow through one project at a time if possible. Also, as Mackenzie suggests,[30] try handling a piece of paper only once before deciding what to do about it and doing it. Keep your mind focused on something that needs your full attention. When one thing does not need your full attention, you may want to double up occasionally if you can do so comfortably by doing such things as exercising while watching TV. Part of pacing yourself is knowing such things as when to take a break to do a different kind of task, when to do some stretching exercises, or when to simply relax and have fun.

Assigning deadlines to tasks is usually very helpful, especially if a public commitment to a deadline is made. Some leeway is to be expected about the deadline, but not enough to encourage procrastination. If you do find yourself procrastinating, it may be that the task seems overwhelming. If so, try breaking the task into small steps and reward yourself generously for completing each step. Also see if perfectionism is causing delays for fear of making a mistake. You may want to review the earlier section on handling perfectionistic behavior if this is contributing to poor time management.

REFERENCES

1. Friedman, M., and Rosenman, R. H. *Type A Behavior and Your Heart.* Greenwich, CT: Fawcett Publications, Inc., 1974.
2. Brallier, L. W. "Suggestions for General Relaxation." Cassette tape, 1978. Available from 621 Maryland Avenue, NE, Washington, DC 20002.
3. Ellis, A., and Harper, R. A. *A New Guide to Rational Living.* North Hollywood: Wilshire Book Company, 1979.
4. Beck, A. T., Rush, J., and Kovacs, M. "Individual Treatment Manual for Cognitive/Behavioral Psychotherapy of Depression." Unpublished manuscript, 1976. Information available from Beck, Department of Psychiatry, University of Pennsylvania.

5. Burns, D. D. *Feeling Good.* New York: William Morrow and Company, Inc., 1980.

6. Ellis, A., and Harper, R. A. *A New Guide to Rational Living.* North Hollywood: Wilshire Book Company, 1979.

7. Beck, A. T., Rush, J., and Kovacs, M. "Individual Treatment Manual for Cognitive/Behavioral Psychotherapy of Depression." Unpublished manuscript, 1976. Information available from Beck, Department of Psychiatry, University of Pennsylvania.

8. Burns, D. D. *Feeling Good.* New York: William Morrow and Company, Inc., 1980.

9. Burns, D. D. *Feeling Good.* New York: William Morrow and Company, Inc., 1980.

10. Burns, D. D. *Feeling Good.* New York: William Morrow and Company, Inc., 1980.

11. Herman, S. J. *Becoming Assertive.* New York: D. Van Nostrand Company, 1978.

12. Alberti, R. E., and Emmons, M. L. *Your Perfect Right.* 2nd ed. San Luis Obispo, CA: Impact Publishers, Inc., 1974.

13. Alberti, R. E., and Emmons, M. L. *Your Perfect Right.* 2nd ed. San Luis Obispo, CA: Impact Publishers, Inc., 1974.

14. Antonovsky, A. *Health, Stress, and Coping.* San Francisco: Jossey-Bass, 1979.

15. Antonovsky, A. *Health, Stress, and Coping.* San Francisco: Jossey-Bass, 1979.

16. Cannon, W. B. *Bodily Changes in Pain, Hunger, Fear, and Rage.* 2nd ed. Boston: Charles T. Branford Co., 1953.

17. Wolf, S., and Goodell, H. eds. *Harold G. Wolff's Stress and Disease.* 2nd ed. Springfield, IL: Thomas, 1968.

18. Wolf, S., and Goodell, H. eds. *Harold G. Wolff's Stress and Disease.* 2nd ed. Springfield, IL: Thomas, 1968.

19. Wolpe, J., and Lazarus, A. A. *Behavior Therapy Techniques.* New York: Pergamon Press, Inc., 1967.

20. Burns, D. D. *Feeling Good.* New York: William Morrow and Company, Inc., 1980.

21. Simonton, O. C., Matthews-Simonton, S., and Creighton, J. *Getting Well Again.* Los Angeles: J. P. Tarcher, Inc., 1978.

22. Benson, H. *The Relaxation Response.* New York: William Morrow and Company, Inc., 1975.

23. Beck, A. T., Rush, J., and Kovacs, M. "Individual Treatment Manual for Cognitive/Behavioral Psychotherapy of Depression." Unpublished manuscript, 1976. Information available from Beck, Department of Psychiatry, University of Pennsylvania.

24. Beck, A. T., Rush, J., and Kovacs, M. "Individual Treatment manual for Cognitive/Behavioral Psychotherapy of Depression." Unpublished manuscript, 1976. Information available from Beck, Department of Psychiatry, University of Pennsylvania.

25. Beck, A. T., Rush, J., and Kovacs, M. "Individual Treatment manual for Cognitive/Behavioral Psychotherapy of Depression." Unpublished manuscript, 1976. Information available from Beck, Department of Psychiatry, University of Pennsylvania.

26. Brallier, L. W. "Suggestions for Restful Sleep." Cassette tape, 1978. Available from 621 Maryland Avenue, NE, Washington, DC 20002.

27. Brallier, L. W. "Suggestions for Restful Sleep." Cassette tape, 1980. Available from 621 Maryland Avenue, NE, Washington, DC 20002.

28. Czeisler, C. A., Weitzman, E. D., Moore-Ede, M. C., Zimmerman, J. C., and Knauer, R. S. "Human Sleep: Its Duration and Organization Depend on Its Circadian Phase." *Science*, 12 December 1980, *210*, 1264-1267.

29. Masters, W. H. and Johnson, V. E. *Human Sexual Inadequacy.* Boston: Little, Brown and Company, 1970.

30. Mackenzie, R. A. *How to Save Two Hours a Day.* Allentown, PA: Day-Timers, 1979.

CHAPTER 6

Stress and the Spirit

Did you notice any strong feelings when you read this chapter's title? Some people may question a separate chapter devoted to spiritual support for managing stress. Inappropriate to a nurse's role to think of these matters . . . ? It's about time we in health care acknowledge this part of the human life experience . . . Leave the spiritual stuff to the religious leaders . . . Good, I want to learn more about enhancing my spiritual experiences and feeling their usefulness in daily life.

Our original spiritual beliefs or our rebellion against those beliefs can be accompanied by intense emotions. The stage is then set for us to become easily threatened during discussions of spiritual concepts. Paradoxically, then, this chapter in a book on stress management may be stressful to read because of the threat involved. Or you may find it affirming and stress-reducing. You may want to take a moment right now to become fully aware of your own reaction to this topic and expectations of this chapter. Write your response to the title, "Stress and the Spirit." Then write your feelings about reading further in this chapter.

In a fairly typical life pattern, a person's energies are likely to be used during their twenties and thirties to establish career, create deeper and/or more relationships with family and friends, and enjoy physical reality. Often little attention is turned to spiritual matters. According to Vaillant, who helped conduct one of the longest studies to date of normal male adult development, there was a pattern in his subjects' religious involvement. Typically, the men in the study were involved in religious pursuits during adolescence, not very involved between twenty and forty, then involved again. As their life cycle evolved, the men assimilated the belief in a "quite invisible trusted power behind the universe ..." [1] To my knowledge, there is no comparable data available for the pattern of spiritual development in women. An informal poll of my social and professional network reveals that women are thought to be more consistently spiritual throughout their life cycle. Even if this is so, I would not be surprised to find that this chapter is more appealing to those of you in your late thirties and up.

Take a few minutes now to review your interest in spiritual development over the years. Has it remained constant? Have there been different stages up to now? Make a few notes about this review. One reason that many people's interest increases in spiritual topics after forty is that by the time we reach forty, most of us have achieved some degree of confidence in managing stressors in our lives. We have practiced managing environmental, physical, mental, emotional, and spiritual stress.

If moderately successful, we have matured from these experiences and feel a sense of some control over our physical existence and how we cope with it. We become able to meet our own wants well enough to direct more energy toward loving others and being more aware of our "inner loving self." This all leaves the way open for focusing some prime quality time and energy on the spiritual part of our lives and ourselves.

You will recall that spirit is one of the personal mediating factors in the conceptual model of stressors and their effects presented in Chapter One. The spiritual part of us includes how we perceive, react to, and cope with stressors. As with the other personal mediating factors, our spiritual side can be a source of stress but it can also play a significant part in coping with stress. We will discuss both of these perspectives.

Earlier I defined spirit as that part of us which can connect with positive forces of the universe or with God, if you will. Positive forces might include such things as art, music, natural surroundings like the ocean, mountains, flowers, animals, and, of course, each other. Our spirit is the essence of our being—it is what makes us human, according to Frankl.[2] He and Jung[3] developed separate schools of thought (logotherapy and Jungian analysis), but agreed that the origin and depth of human spirit is in our unconscious. Our unconscious, then, is a rich source of spiritual experience. When we become aware of this part of our unconscious, we are able to have what Maslow[4] called "peak experiences" or what can be called a sense of unity with the cosmos or oneness with a Higher Being. Maslow's work on self-actualization nurtured the development of a field of psychology known as transpersonal psychology, which deals with spiritual, religious, and mystical experiences and the wholeness of human beings. Transpersonal psychologists are interested in helping people develop as fully as they possibly can. This process includes encouraging them to develop the ability to transcend their own ego boundaries and connect lovingly with others. A large part of this growth process involves assisting people to become thoroughly acquainted with their spiritual consciousness.

An interesting observation from the world of science is a compilation of research by Henry and Stephens[6] which indicates that our capacity for having spiritual experiences may be primarily a function of the hypothalamic limbic complex and right hemisphere of the brain. If so, this would support Jung's concept of archetypes or symbols from the "collective unconscious" of humanity, meaning we all share some similar spiritual or religious or mystical constructs. It does seem that our spiritual self-awareness may have anatomical correlates, giving support to the notion that the spiritual part of us is a "real" and inherent part of our drive toward wholeness.

Now let's define some terms more clearly. I use the words "spiritual" and "religious" to denote two different experiences. *Religious* pertains to an organized group experience of worship and ritual with like-minded individuals for the purpose of recognizing some ultimate reality or deity. *Spiritual* indicates more of a personal experience and style of living oriented toward a sense of connection with a positive Higher Power and the ability to be "tranquil, gentle, and strong."[6] A spiritual lifestyle also is designed to help develop qualities of character such as compassion, love, honesty, and wisdom. A spiritual person draws on these qualities as a source of guidance for daily life experience. This person may or may not belong to an organized religious group.

The other term I wish to clarify is one useful in describing what a person is connecting with when having a spiritual experience, whether through music, or another person, or a sense of oneness with the universe. Some terms describe an *energy*, such as Higher Power or Positive Universal Force, and other terms describe a *being* of some sort, such as Supreme Being, Creator, or God. This energy or this being can be thought of as outside oneself, inside one-self, or both at once. I will be using the term "Greater Power" since it seems to be a term which allows a wide range of individual interpretations. Each of you, then, can read into this term your personal definition and sense of a "Greater Power."

As a Gestalt therapist, I believe that a skeptic and a believer reside in each of us. These two are roughly analogous to our left and right hemispheric brain functions—the left analytical and the right synthesizing into wholeness. This opposition also represents science and spiritual philosophies throughout history. Science is devoted to observing, measuring, manipulating, and predicting physical sensory data. It is concerned with "facts" and "certainty." It is skeptical of data that cannot be gathered by the physical senses. It rarely offers hypotheses about questions related to the meaning of life. Spiritual philosophy and experience are right-hemispheric in nature, transcend sensory experience, and tackle questions about meaning. These, however, cannot be proven in sensory awareness terms because they are irreducible in their own form.

As professionals in health care, all of us have education which helped develop our scientific or left brain functions and encouraged us at times to trust *only* sensory reality. If we were fortunate, we also received a balancing influence of being taught to value and develop our spiritual, intuitive, and creative potential. If both "sides" are developed, some stress can be experienced as a process of bouncing back and forth from a scientific view of existence to a spiritual view. Peaceful integration of these two is the position from which we can most readily handle the stress of living and experience wholeness.

I can now understand why so few health professionals have written about the influence of spiritual philosophy on the process of managing stressors. This chapter was difficult for me to write. It was also highly satisfying. Although I am clearly not a theologian, over the past few years I have become aware that our profession has done little formal thinking about this dimension of humankind and I am glad to contribute a small portion. In exploring spiritual issues with you, however, I am challenging you to pay attention to this area of your life and your beliefs about it. Perhaps your beliefs are approximately what they were when you were a child. Perhaps you have rebelled against those and attached yourself firmly to a new set. Or perhaps you feel unsure about your beliefs. Whatever the case, you may have some strong feelings—both healthy and irrational —attached to your belief system.

We will work in this chapter by asking you assessment questions to help clarify your spiritual belief system. Then more questions will be presented to help you discover how these beliefs help or hinder your ability to manage stressors and attain peace of mind. Then we will go on to a more difficult part. Speaking from the viewpoint of stress management, I will attempt to outline a few beliefs which I or others have seen as inspiring, ineffectual, or deleterious in successfully handling stressors. I will also go on to recommend methods which have proved themselves effective in deepening spiritual experiences of life.

Now, a special word to those of you who are agnos-

tic or atheist in your beliefs. The fact that this chapter
is written from a position which assumes first the existence of a Greater Power and second that we have the
ability to connect with that Power may have already
elicited a fair amount of nausea. As one who was in your
ranks for a number of years (while studying Freud, who
taught that religion was a universal compulsive neurosis,
and even throughout a period when I was diagnosed as
terminally ill), I do understand any impulses you might
have to throw this book aside or write me a note that I
am softheaded and unscientific. But please continue
reading since you will be able to apply the format of this
chapter to your philosophy of life to test its merit as a
support in managing stress.

Assessment of Spiritual Beliefs and Their Effectiveness in Managing Stress

Often, our spiritual beliefs are a bit unclear, rigid, or not
part of our day-to-day awareness. Yet we often guide
our lives using these beliefs as an unspoken basis for decisions.

Following is a model which I use to illustrate the
relationship of spiritual or philosophical concepts and
experiences to thoughts, feelings, and body reactions.

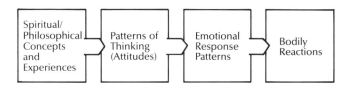

Figure 25: Relationship of spiritual concepts to thoughts, feelings, and body reactions.

Any step of this process can be within or outside of our awareness. These four steps interact with each other in some complicated ways. Basically, however, our beliefs serve as a foundation for our thought patterns and thus our emotional and physical reactions. If the philosophy is strengthening or centering for the person, then the thoughts derived from the philosophy will lead to calm emotional and physical conditions. If the philosophy is weak or inconsistent or negative in nature, the thought patterns will be prone to produce emotional and physical distress. If our beliefs are to be of service to us, we must first be aware of them in all their boldness and subtlety.

Following is a list of statements about the general subject of your spiritual beliefs and values. They are designed to aid you in clarifying these for yourself. Some of the ideas for questions came from the section on life philosophy in Bolles' book *The Three Boxes of Life.* [7] As you can see, there are categories of beliefs with several sentences under each category. Read each sentence and place a mark under the statement that best describes your feelings. There are no right or wrong answers; this exercise is designed only to heighten your awareness. Take your time and allow yourself to ponder as you answer.

BELIEFS/VALUES	Strongly Agree	Agree	Undecided	Disagree	Strongly Disagree

GREATER POWER

A Greater Power exists. —— —— —— —— ——

Nature is part of the Greater
Power. —— —— —— —— ——

The Greater Power is vengeful. —— —— —— —— ——

The Greater Power is loving. —— —— —— —— ——

The Greater Power is impersonal. —— —— —— —— ——

The Greater Power created the
universe. —— —— —— —— ——

The Greater Power appears in
many forms. —— —— —— —— ——

The Greater Power is all-
powerful and always present. —— —— —— —— ——

The Greater Power has a sense
of humor. —— —— —— —— ——

The Greater Power must have
praise and adoration or will
become wrathful. —— —— —— —— ——

The Greater Power allows
eternal life to only a
chosen few. —— —— —— —— ——

The Greater Power could be
overcome by evil. —— —— —— —— ——

The Greater Power is pure,
positive, loving energy. —— —— —— —— ——

The Greater Power is in control of all creation. —— —— —— —— ——

The Greater Power is
forgiving. —— —— —— —— ——

MYSELF AND THE GREATER POWER

The Greater Power is external
to me. —— —— —— —— ——

The Greater Power is inside me. —— —— —— —— ——

I can connect with the
Greater Power. —— —— —— —— ——

The Greater Power knows me
as a person. —— —— —— —— ——

BELIEFS/VALUES	Strongly Agree	Agree	Undecided	Disagree	Strongly Disagree
I must obey the laws of the Greater Power or be punished.	—	—	—	—	—
I am loved unconditionally by the Greater Power.	—	—	—	—	—
The Greater Power hears my prayers.	—	—	—	—	—
I am rewarded by the Greater Power for doing good things.	—	—	—	—	—
I will be sentenced to hell by the Greater Power if I sin too much.	—	—	—	—	—
I am afraid of the Greater Power.	—	—	—	—	—
The Greater Power controls my life.	—	—	—	—	—
The Greater Power can cause me to be ill or die.	—	—	—	—	—
My connection with the Greater Power gives me hope and courage.	—	—	—	—	—
My relationship to the Greater Power is the most meaningful thing in my life.	—	—	—	—	—
I have experienced oneness with the Greater Power.	—	—	—	—	—
The Greater Power knows my thoughts and may punish me for them.	—	—	—	—	—
The Greater Power is with me when I am in crisis.	—	—	—	—	—
At the time of death I will be in the presence of the Greater Power.	—	—	—	—	—
Knowledge of the Greater Power gives me a life purpose.	—	—	—	—	—

BELIEFS/VALUES	Strongly Agree	Agree	Undecided	Disagree	Strongly Disagree

MYSELF

	Strongly Agree	Agree	Undecided	Disagree	Strongly Disagree
I have a place in the cosmos.	—	—	—	—	—
I have purposes in life.	—	—	—	—	—
Joy is part of spiritual life.	—	—	—	—	—
Compassion is an important spiritual characteristic.	—	—	—	—	—
I am hateful toward myself.	—	—	—	—	—
I am strong.	—	—	—	—	—
I am gentle.	—	—	—	—	—
I am critical of myself.	—	—	—	—	—
I am committed to living fully.	—	—	—	—	—
I am a sinner.	—	—	—	—	—
I am a loving person.	—	—	—	—	—
I find meaning in any suffering I go through.	—	—	—	—	—
I secretly think I know *the* truth about spiritual matters.	—	—	—	—	—
I am born again.	—	—	—	—	—
I am excited about being alive.	—	—	—	—	—
Creation continues in me.	—	—	—	—	—
Honesty is important to me.	—	—	—	—	—
I am forgiving of my own mistakes.	—	—	—	—	—
I am valuable as an individual.	—	—	—	—	—
When I die, I will simply cease to exist.	—	—	—	—	—
When I die, my consciousness will survive death.	—	—	—	—	—
I feel a great sense of peace of mind.	—	—	—	—	—
Wholeness is possible for me.	—	—	—	—	—
I am hopeful about my life and myself.	—	—	—	—	—
I have gifts and talents yet to be used.	—	—	—	—	—

BELIEFS/VALUES	Strongly Agree	Agree	Undecided	Disagree	Strongly Disagree
I am open to spiritual growth.	—	—	—	—	—

OTHERS

	Strongly Agree	Agree	Undecided	Disagree	Strongly Disagree
People have no particular intrinsic value.	—	—	—	—	—
People are basically being guided toward perfection.	—	—	—	—	—
People can easily turn evil.	—	—	—	—	—
Each person has a part of the Greater Power inside.	—	—	—	—	—
Each person has a different path to the Greater Power.	—	—	—	—	—
People are born in sin.	—	—	—	—	—
People are generally ignorant about spiritual life.	—	—	—	—	—
All human life is sacred.	—	—	—	—	—
People can be spiritual without being religious.	—	—	—	—	—
Each person is precious to the Greater Power.	—	—	—	—	—

MYSELF AND OTHERS

	Strongly Agree	Agree	Undecided	Disagree	Strongly Disagree
I love all people.	—	—	—	—	—
I compete with others.	—	—	—	—	—
I want to be known for my religious/spiritual beliefs.	—	—	—	—	—
I can find and relate to the most spiritual parts of others.	—	—	—	—	—
I feel a strong sense of unity with all other people.	—	—	—	—	—
I forgive people easily.	—	—	—	—	—
I often wish others well.	—	—	—	—	—
I only trust people of my own religious faith.	—	—	—	—	—
I must look to those in authority for my spiritual knowledge.	—	—	—	—	—

BELIEFS/VALUES	Strongly Agree	Agree	Undecided	Disagree	Strongly Disagree
I am honest in my relationships with others.	—	—	—	—	—
I feel it is my duty to share my beliefs.	—	—	—	—	—
I feel somewhat superior to others in my spiritual growth.	—	—	—	—	—
I am compassionate toward others.	—	—	—	—	—

ENVIRONMENT

	Strongly Agree	Agree	Undecided	Disagree	Strongly Disagree
The universe was designed by the Greater Power.	—	—	—	—	—
The universe just is, and has been, and will be.	—	—	—	—	—
There is a purpose for the universe.	—	—	—	—	—
There is no particular reason for planet earth to exist.	—	—	—	—	—
Nature is basically hostile and uncaring.	—	—	—	—	—
Nature is wise.	—	—	—	—	—

MYSELF AND THE ENVIRONMENT

	Strongly Agree	Agree	Undecided	Disagree	Strongly Disagree
I feel a sense of oneness with nature at times.	—	—	—	—	—
Reality is only what I know with information from my senses.	—	—	—	—	—
Reality is everything I perceive sensorily and with my intuition.	—	—	—	—	—
I am an important part of the universal level of things.	—	—	—	—	—
There is beauty all around me.	—	—	—	—	—
Animals are basically unfeeling and inferior to me.	—	—	—	—	—
I am in awe of things sometimes.	—	—	—	—	—

After completing this section, take a moment to reflect on some of your answers. Did any of your responses surprise you? Disappoint you? Delight you?

Now that you have sharpened your awareness of your spiritual beliefs and values, let's take a look at how these beliefs and values help you manage the stress in your life. Listed below are some possible statements about you.

Begin each sentence with the words "Generally speaking, my beliefs," and complete it with each phrase supplied. Read each statement and mark whether that statement is almost always true, sometimes true, or almost never true for your spiritual beliefs and values.

GENERALLY SPEAKING, MY BELIEFS	Almost Always	Sometimes	Almost Never
. . . support a low-stress lifestyle.	___	___	___
. . . help me have peace of mind.	___	___	___
. . . induce guilt at times.	___	___	___
. . . free me.	___	___	___
. . . give me a sense of purpose in life.	___	___	___
. . . help me love others.	___	___	___
. . . support my connection with the Greater Power.	___	___	___
. . . help me relax.	___	___	___
. . . fill me with joy.	___	___	___
. . . sustain me through times of suffering.	___	___	___
. . . lead to pessimism about life.	___	___	___
. . . are confusing.	___	___	___
. . . lead me into conflict with myself.	___	___	___
. . . help me be more responsible.	___	___	___
. . . leave me feeling empty.	___	___	___
. . . give me a headache.	___	___	___
. . . are the opposite of my parents' beliefs.	___	___	___
. . . help me establish my goals in life.	___	___	___
. . . are shared by many.	___	___	___
. . . reflect my knowledge of ultimate truth.	___	___	___

	Almost Always	Sometimes	Almost Never
. . . help me gain a sense of loving detachment from many events and people.	—	—	—
. . . satisfy me.	—	—	—
. . . bring persecution from others.	—	—	—
. . . stimulate further spiritual progress.	—	—	—
. . . help me with situations of daily living.	—	—	—
. . . are different from anyone else's I know about.	—	—	—
. . . help me respect myself.	—	—	—
. . . support me through difficult times.	—	—	—
. . . lead to bouts of depression.	—	—	—
. . . isolate me from the mainstream.	—	—	—
. . . help me love myself.	—	—	—
. . . cause me to tense my muscles and grind my teeth.	—	—	—
. . . give me support in dealing with losses.	—	—	—
. . . allow me to let others find their own spiritual path.	—	—	—
. . . create a consciousness of fear in me.	—	—	—
. . . are evolving/changing.	—	—	—
. . . cause me to worry about others' beliefs—especially loved ones.	—	—	—
. . . explain why certain tragedies happen.	—	—	—
. . . help me play a martyr role in life.	—	—	—
. . . help me solve my problems.	—	—	—
. . . help me deny my problems.	—	—	—
. . . give my life meaning.	—	—	—
. . . help me be compassionate.	—	—	—
. . . support negative thinking.	—	—	—
. . . respect others' ability to care for themselves.	—	—	—
. . . allow me to see myself as a worthwhile human being.	—	—	—
. . . teach me to feel ashamed of myself.	—	—	—
. . . help me make amends when necessary.	—	—	—
. . . help me take time for myself.	—	—	—
. . . insist that I treat myself with love and respect.	—	—	—

	Almost Always	Sometimes	Almost Never
. . . bring a sense of balance into my life.	___	___	___
. . . induce anxiety.	___	___	___
. . . allow me to see the humor in life.	___	___	___
. . . help me gain a sense of perspective in life.	___	___	___
. . . help me to learn from my experiences, both positive and negative.	___	___	___
. . . help me establish priorities in my life.	___	___	___
. . . provide a sense of hope.	___	___	___
. . . induce a great deal of stress.	___	___	___
. . . help me search for meaning in tragedies.	___	___	___
. . . help me feel serene.	___	___	___
. . . help me know my inner self.	___	___	___
. . . allow me to forgive myself.	___	___	___
. . . make sense to me.	___	___	___
. . . comfort me.	___	___	___

Can you see more clearly now what your beliefs are and how they help or hinder your movement toward a lifestyle of managing stress successfully? I realize this may seem like a very utilitarian view of spiritual values; however, it is based on my own belief that spiritual concepts lived out in daily life lead us toward wholeness and peace rather than toward distress. This is not to say that the *process* of spiritual growth and change is not stressful at times. Furthermore, I believe that if a spiritual belief or value does not help you to manage stress and gain peace of mind, it is probably neurotic in nature or at least counterproductive. In arguing for an empirical approach to judging religion and against a historical approach, William James, in his book *The Varieties of Religious Experience*, supports this utilitarian view of spiritual concepts by agreeing with Jonathan Edwards' statement, "By their fruits ye shall know them, not by their roots."[8]

Do you recall a time in your life when you were in a spiritual crisis? If so, you can recapture the sense of diminished coherence, sense of futility, lack of direction, exhaustion, lack of a sense of connection with a Greater Power, depression, inability to feel a purpose in life, and more. In my clinical practice I often see people with cancer who suffer severe pain and have been told they are going to die. If they have little spiritual support or believe that the disease is a punishment from God, they are vulnerable to the distress of a crisis as just described. Certainly there are many entry points into crisis if spiritual support is absent or turned into a negative influence.

In *Stress Without Distress*, [9] Selye gives some guidelines for managing stress that have a spiritual tone. Among these is to avoid hatred and the urge for revenge since these emotions will lead to great distress. (See Chapter Five for suggestions on this topic.) Selye also promotes the philosophy which he calls altruistic egotism or Earning Thy Neighbor's Love as a way of lowering one's distress level. He even goes so far as to suggest that pleasing God is a way to satisfy basic drives and reduce distress. Also suggested are loyally adhering to a code of honor and exchanging joy with others.

Over the years of my practice and teaching, I have seen three general categories of influence of spiritual beliefs. These can be called inspiring, ineffectual, and deleterious.

Inspiring beliefs lead to the excitement of growth and the possibility of experiencing unity with the Greater Power. The resulting peace of mind is a strong, quiet force that prevents and opposes the stress response. We will discuss this category in greater detail in the next section of this chapter.

Ineffectual beliefs are those that are colorless and

do not harm or help in daily living or in times of crisis. Usually people who experience their beliefs in this way borrowed someone else's beliefs as their own. Introjected beliefs are not integrated so are of little or no support. Some people experience nearly everything intellectually, including their spiritual beliefs. This also leads to little perceived spiritual support. People in their early adulthood and those who have not suffered a serious crisis in life may not have developed their spiritual belief system, so find it lacking when they do want support. One of my clients, a chemical engineer in a highly stressful state, replied to my inquiry about his spiritual beliefs with, "I never really thought about them much. I think I believe in ghosts, though—does that count?" We started there.

Deleterious beliefs are those that engender distress. At times people take sacred teachings and twist them a bit until distorted negative beliefs are created. These beliefs cause fear, anger, guilt, anxiety, depression, and/ or a host of physical problems and interpersonal conflicts. The very people suffering these stress symptoms may go ahead to teach these negative and destructive beliefs to others.

Scott Peck, a psychiatrist who wrote about spiritual growth in *The Road Less Traveled*, acknowledges that belief in God has been associated with some very stressful events.

> There is clearly a lot of dirty bath water surrounding the reality of God. Holy wars. Inquisitions. Animal sacrifice. Human sacrifice. Superstition. Stultification. Dogmatism. Ignorance. Hypocrisy. Self-righteousness. Rigidity. Cruelty. Book-burning. Witch-burning. Inhibition. Fear. Conformity. Morbid guilt. Insanity. The list is almost endless.

But is all this what God has done to humans or what
humans have done to God? It is abundantly evident
that belief in God is often destructively dogmatic.
Is the problem, then, that humans tend to believe in
God, or is the problem that humans tend to be dogmatic? Anyone who has known a dyed-in-the-wool
atheist will know that such an individual can be as
dogmatic about unbelief as any believer can be
about belief. Is it belief in God we need to get rid
of, or is it dogmatism? [10]

Fear of punishment by a vengeful God and acting
out a "sacred" suffering martyr role are two of the most
common dysfunctional results of "dirty bath water" beliefs I have seen. Being told consistently that one is a
miserable sinner (especially while being led in prayer, a
state of consciousness in which one is vulnerable to suggestion) can certainly lead to destructive results in terms
of stress. Believing that you can do no good leads to
interpreting many of one's own acts and even one's own
thoughts as sins, which, in turn, fosters crippling guilt
and extraordinarily low self-esteem. Occasionally someone can counteract these stressful effects by having
strong beliefs that the Greater Power forgives all sins.

The martyr role can be played out in a countless
number of ways. A common religious martyr role is to
silently suffer the knowledge of "truth." People who
believe they have discovered *the* way can suffer great
distress from not being able to get other people to join
them in their belief. A life of frustration and disappoint-
ment can shadow these people who then often defen-
sively adopt a martyred small-forces-of-good-against-
large-forces-of-evil role. As many nurses know, trying to
"save" other people, whether by attempting to force
upon them new spiritual beliefs or new patterns of self-

care for their health, often results only in high distress for the nurse.

The next section of this chapter focuses on actively building your own spiritual support to help manage both day-to-day and crisis-situation stress. Obviously, every suggestion will not feel right for you. As in other sections, I have tried to include the suggestions and exercises I have seen as most helpful to most people, but it is important that you feel free to reject some or all of them if you wish.

Management of Stress from a Spiritual Perspective

The exercises you just did—clarifying beliefs and values and assessing their support in managing stress—are a process rather than an end point. Clarifying your beliefs and understanding how your beliefs affect you are essential for feeling well-grounded and secure. Another factor to consider is whether or not your friends and family support the beliefs you feel are right for you. "Holy wars" of all sizes are common in world history and can be extremely stressful when they tear the fabric of family ties. It is wise to avoid the position of maintaining certain spiritual beliefs as part of a battle for individuation. If your true beliefs and experience separate you from loved ones, it would probably reduce your stress level significantly to find others who are on a spiritual pilgrimage similar to yours.

This section is devoted to building the strength of your own unique spiritual consciousness. I will outline methods you can use to deepen your spiritual experiences, but the journey is exclusively yours. You must find your own meaning in it. Perhaps you are already familiar with this kind of growth, or maybe you have rarely been exposed to ideas about your own spiritual development. Whatever the case, you may want to experiment with the idea of "treating" yourself to a view of your life and yourself from this angle. If much of this is new for you, your autonomic nervous system and endocrine system may react to the challenge and the excitement of special "spiritual moments." In the long run, though, your experiment will probably yield calming revitalization.

Some say the Greater Power is outside us, some say it is inside, and some say the Greater Power is everywhere—we are in It at all times. No matter what is believed about the "location," there is definite agreement that the point of spiritual growth is to *connect* with this Greater Power. How do people do this? Many attend churches, synagogues, or temples. Others read books, join prayer groups and study groups, find a teacher, or practice spiritual disciplines on their own. The remainder of this chapter will describe practices such as prayer, meditation, contemplation, imagery, and healing. See what you think might be useful to you.

In attempts to communicate with the Greater Power, we basically communicate outwardly as in some form of prayer and/or we try to receive communication by such endeavors as meditation, contemplation, and imagery. During these attempts to connect with the Greater Power, people quite often experience what is described as a shift in consciousness. William James, in *Varieties of Religious Experience*, speaks of a wakeful state and prayer state of consciousness:

> "The whole drift of my education goes to persuade me that the world of our present consciousness is only one out of many worlds of consciousness that exist, and that those other worlds must contain experiences which have a

meaning for our life also; and that although in the main their experiences are those of this world keep discrete, yet the two become continuous at certain points, and higher energies filter in."[11]

Stanley Krippner, in a paper on altered states of consciousness,[12] identifies nineteen states of consciousness other than our usual alert wakeful one. Among these are dreaming, sleeping, hyperalert, daydreaming, coma, trance, meditative, and expanded consciousness. Krippner describes connecting with the Greater Power as follows:

> At the integral level (which relatively few individuals attain), there is a religious and/or mystical experience in which God (or the "ground of being") is confronted or in which the individual has the subjective impression of dissolving into the energy field of the universe (e.g., "satori," "samadhi," "oceanic unity," "cosmic consciousness," "peak experience").[13]

As you can see, there are many potential states of consciousness for us to experience. Our shifts are not always under control. In my clinical work I have seen people who have been on a spiritual path for many years and want to experience "oceanic unity" but have not been able to. On the other hand, I have seen clients who appear to be predominantly left-brained and uninterested in spiritual quests but report unitive experiences from only a few sessions of biofeedback. In the past few years I have begun to warn these "left-brained" people that they may be innocently practicing their handwarming and suddenly experience oneness with the universe!

Now let's turn to the process of connecting with the Greater Power by active outwardly directed communication. Many do this through prayer, either alone or in groups. These prayers usually begin by addressing the Greater Power and then giving thanks, asking forgiveness, asking for blessings, and/or asking for healing. The prayer can be formal and ritualized or be of a casual and conversational tone. The sense of actually connecting with the Greater Power varies tremendously among people who use this method.

People from around the world have used music and chanting as ways to alter their consciousness and attempt to communicate to the Greater Power. Others devote themselves to living a lifestyle of reaching out to fellow human beings in a helpful way, in part as a means of communicating with the Greater Power. Fox, in writing on American-style spirituality, defines prayer as a lifestyle of "live-loving, life-sharing spirituality."[14] He encourages people to go beyond the idea of prayer as talking to God and experience prayer as a synthesis of their personal and political lives. In this way they will connect with the Greater Power.

In addition to actively communicating outwardly, many people feel comfortable with more passive methods of connecting with the Greater Power. Some people stay alert for "messages" from the Greater Power, which may come to them at any time of the day and in many forms. An example of this is a client of mine who has cancer. At the beginning of therapy she was skeptical about the possibility that reducing her distress level could support her immune system to be more active. She reported in the next session that she had gone home from our session and had prayed to God to send her a sign about whether to trust me and my ideas or not. When she finished praying, she felt an uncontrollable urge to get up and turn on television even though she did not usually watch it at that hour. She tuned in to an interview with a well-known physician. She heard the physician say that current research demonstrates a relationship between high levels of stress and a diminished capacity of the immune system, relevant information for physicians to consider in the treatment of cancer. My client laughed heartily as she reported this incident, saying she had never got an answer to a prayer so fast in all her life. She wanted to begin therapy immediately.

Another way people feel they get messages from the Greater Power is through trance mediums, who supposedly relay messages via "spirits" they are able to contact. Still other people feel they get communication through direct inspiration, such as an "Aha!" thought from "out of the blue" while they are going through their usual daily routine. Many people believe that we often say and do "inspired" things to and for each other and that we only need stay open to the idea for it to happen. Some of you may have experienced clients saying to you, in effect, "God must have led you to tell me that." A client said to me recently, "I know God was working through you when you recommended this book to me because it has changed my life so much for the better."

Let's turn now to the ancient methods of opening ourselves to connecting with the Greater Power—prayer, contemplation, meditation, and imagery. These are the traditional tools of spiritual development, which span thousands of years and spring from every religion known to us. Definitions of these activities overlap like the leaves of an artichoke so I will present the methods without concern for labels others might use. There is also little agreement among philosophers, theologians, psychologists, and mystics about whether the experiences resulting from these traditional spiritual methods are of the Greater Power directly or of one's own unconscious or "higher self." See what your own experience tells you.

Most methods of open, receptive awareness involve focusing the mind. This "one pointedness," as it is called in the Eastern tradition, helps increase the power of our mind to grasp altered state experiences. In biofeedback terms, the brainwaves slow to an alpha or theta rate as measured in cycles per second, allowing experiences other than the linear, rational ones of our usual beta state. We all have these receptive, focused moments spontaneously during a day, and they can be spiritual if, for instance, the focus is on a beautiful product of nature or on a particularly joyful thought.

Intentional focusing of awareness for spiritual purposes can take the form of contemplating on a word, concept, or experience. You may want to try some contemplative methods. To practice intentional focusing, choose a time and place when you can be free from disturbance and sit quietly. Get comfortable so you can breathe easily and relax your body, letting go of your awareness of the process (which might interrupt your concentration). Choose a focus for your awareness. One choice could be a word that describes a personal characteristic you would like to emphasize, such as courage, love, or compassion. Another might be a concept, such as grace, soul, forgiveness, or white light. Other possibilities are to focus on the Greater Power, the organization of the universe, or on a cell of your body and how it works. Yet another possibility is to read inspirational literature or a favorite poem and use as your focus whatever words or phrases attract your attention. To keep your awareness focused, occasionally say or think the object of your contemplation. When extraneous thoughts occur, just acknowledge that your attention has wandered, and let the thoughts go as you refocus your awareness.

Practicing in this manner for about ten minutes at a time is enough for most people to benefit from the experience. Occasionally you may feel a sense of experiencing some of the qualities of the Greater Power, but do not be discouraged if you have not reached nirvana by the third try. Contemplation is simple but not easy. A disciplined approach is very helpful. Sitting down at a certain time or times of the day with regularity is important. Eventually you may find yourself in a fairly constant state of receptivity to the Greater Power from your contemplative practice, but this takes time and there is no quick, easy method.

Choosing an external object for contemplation can lead to the same rewards. A sunrise, sunset, flower, sleeping baby, or whatever you choose can provide inspiration for this type of focusing. If you try this type of contemplation, avoid staring at the object. Instead, let your gaze softly rest on the object for about ten minutes, allowing your eyes to blink as necessary.

Another subject you might choose to observe is yourself. Sit comfortably with your eyes closed and imagine you are outside yourself simply looking without making judgments. Let yourself notice whatever you observe—your body, your thoughts, your feelings, and so forth. Also notice when you make judgments and just let them go and refocus.

A further way to expand your consciousness and connect with the Greater Power is to contemplate being in another person's life position. Select someone quite different from yourself and attempt to see the world through his or her eyes.

Imagery is often a creative path in spiritual development. You may want to try sitting in a relaxed position with your eyes closed and visualizing the face of a loving and wise old woman or man, or try imagining Christ or Buddha or even a being of light. Imagine a dialogue with your image in which you ask questions relevant to your spiritual journey. You may want to make notes in a journal you keep of these "conversations" if you do this regularly. A related method is to see your own essence as a bright white light which radiates loving acceptance, forgiveness, and respect toward yourself and others.

An advanced method of receptiveness to the Greater Power is one in which you open with a short prayer, then be still and listen as if waiting for a whisper or voice in the distance. This can be an experience of profound silence in which you feel a sense of harmony with all that is. On the way to that silence you may spontaneously "see" symbols that are significant in their meaning to you.

As unlikely as it may seem, taking quiet time to focus on the idea of your own death, even if momentarily stressful, may lead to greater peace. Our death is a highly charged emotional and spiritual issue, which can engender sufficient fear to retard spiritual growth. You may spontaneously begin to face the issue of your death as you practice contemplation and meditation, or you may want to deal with it intentionally by using the subject of your own death as a focus for contemplation. You may also want to visualize yourself after death if you subscribe to the idea of an afterlife. Coming to comfortable terms with your own death can add an immeasurable sense of peace and vitality to your life and replace much of the conscious and unconscious distress connected with the thought of death.

Healing oneself or another through prayer is an ancient way of connecting with the Greater Power. Healing by the laying on of hands is a similar ancient tradition. Both of these forms of healing are practiced in many religious ceremonies and by many who are in the process of spiritual growth.

Contemporary psychologists, physicists, religious leaders, and nurses are researching the topic of self-healing and are publishing their results. Stanley Krippner and Alberto Villoldo [15] in their book *Realms of Healing* provide an international perspective on healing. In a section on how healing occurs, the authors explore various explanations for the phenomenon of healing as documented in the physical sciences as well as by psychological, psychic, and spiritual paradigms.

The act of healing may be experienced as a spiritual experience, a psychic event, or a knowledgeable clinical process. Dolores Krieger, Ph.D., R.N., of New York University, conceptualizes the healing process as derived from but different than the spiritual practice of laying on of hands. In *The Therapeutic Touch* [16] she refers to healing energy and the energy field around our bodies, which can be influenced by a "healer's" energy. Dr. Krieger clearly outlines the healing process as one of centering, assessing the energy field, "unruffling" the field, and directing the transfer of energy to the client. Some years ago, Dr. Krieger formally organized what is now known as the Nurse Healers-Professional Associates Cooperative, which sponsors annual national assemblies on healing and forms a national network for those interested in learning and practicing healing. [17]

As a spiritual experience, healing by prayer or through physical contact can be an extraordinary loving and connecting experience both with another person and the Greater Power. [18]

In *The Aquarian Conspiracy*, Marilyn Ferguson addresses the personal and social transformation she sees for the 1980s.[19] She devotes a chapter to our quest in this era of history to try to "connect with the source" as well as noting how many thousands of people are transforming their knowledge, values, and consciousness. The fact that so many people are in a process of transformation involving their consciousness lends itself to the formation of groups whose members seek to support each other in their transformation process. Some currently popular writings that are easily adapted to a group study format are Assagioli's *Psychosynthesis*,[20] Progoff's *The Well and the Cathedral*,[21] and a program of study called *The Course in Miracles* from the Foundation for Inner Peace.[22]

Transformative processes can be exhilaratingly positive but are not without their pain and stress. Assagioli says:

> Spiritual development is a long and arduous journey, an adventure through strange lands full of surprises, joy, and beauty, difficulties, and even dangers. It involves the awakening of potentialities hitherto dormant, the raising of consciousness to new realms, a dramatic transmutation of the "normal" elements of the personality, and a functioning along a new inner dimension.[23]

In this article, Assagioli outlines disturbances that can arise at various phases of spiritual development and addresses the issue of how to deal with these problems.

Now for the positive results. Generally speaking, once people avoid the common pitfalls along the spiritual path, such as cults, their own temptation to become self-righteous, and selfishness in the use of spiritual insights, they usually report that their spiritual journey strengthened and matured their personality. This, of course, is of major benefit in managing stressors of all kinds. Maslow studied people who reported having transcendent experiences, which he called "peak experiences."[24] In his book *Religions, Values and Peak Experiences*[25] he speaks of the religious aspects of peak experiences. Following are some of his findings.

The person himself tends to move toward fusion, integration, and unity, and away from splitting, conflicts, and oppositions.

In the peak experiences, there tends to be a loss, even though transient, of fear, anxiety, inhibition, of defense and control, of perplexity, confusion, conflict, of delay and restraint. The profound fear of disintegration, of insanity, of death, all tend to disappear for the moment. Perhaps this amounts to saying that fear disappears.

In peak experiences, there is a tendency to move more closely to a perfect identity, or uniqueness, or to the idiosyncracy of the person or to his real self, to have become more a real person.

. . . a peculiar change which can best be described as nonevaluating, noncomparing, or nonjudging cognition.

In the peak experiences, we become more detached, more objective, and are more able to perceive the world as if it were independent not only of the perceiver but even of human beings in general.

He becomes less an object, less a thing, less a thing of the world living under the laws of the physical

world, and he becomes more a psyche, more a person, more subject to the psychological laws, especially the laws of what people have called the "higher life."

The world seen in the peak experiences is seen only
as beautiful, good, desirable, worthwhile, etc. and is
never experienced as evil or undesirable. The world
is accepted.

The peak experiencer becomes more loving and accepting, and so he becomes more spontaneous and
honest and innocent.

Maslow says the range of after-effects of these experiences is wide though at times the effects are so profound that they permanently change the person.

You can see that any of these transcendent experiences, if it impacts on the personality, could help a
person manage stress in his or her life. Detachment may
be a key. The ability to detach yourself from the world
—to be an observer of it—allows a sense of humor and
a nonjudgmental attitude. Joy comes too when the main
connection is with one's own "higher" self or the Greater Power, and freedom is gained from material goods,
cultural mores, and other sources of possible distress.

In this chapter we have explored what your spiritual
beliefs and values are and how they influence your patterns of managing stress. Some methods of deepening
the spiritual aspect of your life were suggested. Was this
chapter what you expected? Can you see any applica-
tions of whatever you may have learned to your daily
personal and professional life?

Throughout this book the concept of wholeness has
been emphasized in relationship to coping well with

stress. We have studied your environment, body, mind, and now even your spirit, recognizing the intimate relationship of each of these with the others. We have discussed ways to prevent stress, work it off, let it go, and accommodate to it. The most generally effective way to live allows us to integrate all these parts and ways into a strong unitive human being. From this vantage point of wholeness, we have the highest probability of successfully managing stress.

REFERENCES

1. Vaillant, G. E. *Adaptation to Life.* Boston: Little, Brown and Company, 1977.

2. Frankl, V. E. *The Unconscious God.* New York: Simon and Schuster, 1975.

3. Jung, C. G. *The Undiscovered Self.* New York: Mentor Books, 1958.

4. Maslow, A. H. *Religions, Values, and Peak-Experiences.* New York: Penguin Books, 1977.

5. Henry, J. P., and Stephens, P. M. *Stress, Health, and the Social Environment.* New York: Springer-Verlag, 1977.

6. Underhill, E. *The Spiritual Life.* New York: Harper and Row, Publishers.

7. Bolles, R. N., *The Three Boxes of Life.* Berkeley: Ten Speed Press, 1978.

8. James, W. *The Varieties of Religious Experience.* (New York: Macmillan Publishing Co., Inc., 1976.

9. Selye, H. *Stress Without Distress.* New York: The New American Library, Inc., 1975.

10. Peck, M. S. *The Road Less Traveled.* New York: Simon and Schuster, 1978.

11. James, W. *The Varieties of Religious Experience.* New York: Macmillan Publishing Co., Inc., 1976.

12. White, J. *The Highest State of Consciousness.* New York: Anchor Books, 1972.

13. White, J. *The Highest State of Consciousness.* New York: Anchor Books, 1972.

14. Fox, M. *On Becoming a Musical Mystical Bear.* New York: Paulist Press, 1976.

15. Krippner, S., and Villoldo, A. *The Realms of Healing.* Millbrae, CA: Celestial Arts, 1976.

16. Krieger, D. *The Therapeutic Touch.* Englewood Cliffs, NJ: Prentice-Hall, Inc., 1979.

17. Nurse Healers Professional Associates Cooperative, Box 7, 70 Shelley Avenue, Port Chester, NY 10573.

18. Brallier, L. W. "The Process of Healing: Theme of a Spiritual Journey." *Military Chaplains' Review "Spiritual Journeying,"* Fall 1980, pp. 91-97.

19. Ferguson, M. *The Aquarian Conspiracy: Personal and Social Transformation in the 1980s.* Los Angeles: J. P. Tarcher, Inc., 1980.

20. Assagioli, R. *Psychosynthesis.* New York: Penguin Books, 1976.

21. Progoff, I. *The Well and the Cathedral.* New York: Dialogue House Library, 1977.

22. *Course in Miracles*, Vol. 1. New York: Foundation for Inner Peace, 1977.

23. Assagioli, R. Self-realization and Psychological Disturbances. *Synthesis, 3-4,* 1977, 148-171.

24. Maslow, A. H. *Religions, Values, and Peak Experiences.* New York: Penguin Books, 1977.

25. Maslow, A. H. *Religions, Values, and Peak-Experiences.* New York: Penguin Books, 1977.

Index

ABC theory of rational-
    emotive therapy, 189-190
Abdominal breathing, 140
Accidents, avoidance of, 88-89
Accident-proneness, 61
Accommodation
    as a method of coping with
        stress, 185-186
    to environmental stressors,
        67
Achterberg, J., 137
Acid secretion in the stomach,
    57
ACTH. *See* Adrenocortico-
    tropic hormone
Acupressure, 142, 143-145
Acupuncture, 145
Acute psychosis, 164
Adaptation energy, 2, 51

Adaptive hormones, 55, 59
Addiction
    and assertive behavior, 238
    to alcohol, 237-238
    to stress, 26-27
Addictive behavior, 164,
    237-239
    as a stress-reducer, 61-62
    assessment of, 177-179
    management of, using
        imagery, 239
Additives in food, 121
Adrenal cortex, 40
Adrenal glands, 40, 46, 57
Adrenal-cortical enlargement,
    51
Adrenal-medullary reaction, 49
Adrenal-medullary system, 40,
    42

Adrenaline, 46, 59, 87
Adrenocorticotropic hormone
    (ACTH), 54-55, 56, 60
Aggressive behavior, 196
Alarm reaction phase of
    general adaptation syn-
    drome, 50, 175
Alberti, R. E., 197
Alcohol addiction, 237-238
    assessment of, 177-179
Alcoholics Anonymous, 178,
    179, 238
Alertness, regulation of, 34
Allergens in food, 121
Altered states of conscious-
    ness, 270, 271
Altruistic egotism, 265
Amygdala, 37-38, 44
Anderson, B., 126
Anger, 163, 207-213
Antibodies, 59
Anti-inflammatory hormones,
    55
Antonovsky, A., 9, 200
Anxiety, 131, 162, 216-222
Apathy, 163
Aquarian Conspiracy, The,
    276-277
Arousal
    level, 36
    state, 44
Arteriosclerosis, 48, 56
Arthritis, influence of stress
    on, 58-59
Asanas, 141
Ascorbic acid, 120
Assagioli, R., 277
Assertive behavior, 196-199,
    215-216
    and addiction, 238
Atkins, R., 118
Attitudes. *See* Negative atti-
    tudes
Authority
    assessment of pattern of,
    169

dealing with, 169-170
Autogenics, 134-136
Automatic thoughts, 190
Autonomic nervous system,
    39, 40, 46
    effect on organs, 46-47
Autonomy, 169
Awareness
    of a Greater Power, 273
    of personal feelings, 201,
    202
*Awareness Through Move-
    ment,* 141

Balance, 181, 184
Ballentine, R., 120
Basal ganglia, 36
Beck, A. T., 189, 190
Beck Depression Inventory,
    223-227
Becoming Assertive, 196
Behavior
    aggressive, 196
    assertive, 196-199, 215-216
    theory, rational-emotive,
    189-190
    therapists, 189
    See also Conservation-
    withdrawal pattern of
Behavioral signs of distress,
    164
Beliefs, personal
    self-regulation of, 189-200
Beliefs, spiritual
    as a way to manage stress,
    264-279
    assessment of, 254, 255-
    264
    categories of influence of,
    265-266
Benson, H., 221
Benson's relaxation response
    method, 139, 220-221
Berrien, F. K., 76
Bioenergetics, 141

Biofeedback, 21, 39, 130-132
    in management of head-
        aches, 150-151
Biological condition, obtain-
    ing information regarding,
    130
Biorhythms, 112-115
Blood flow, restriction of, 48
Blood pressure, 40, 46, 48,
    49, 130
Blood sugar level, 59
Blood vessels, thickening of,
    48
Blood volume, 40
Body
    effect of stress on, 40-62
    psychophysiology review
        of, 33-40
    signs of burnout in, 17
Body distress
    assessment of, 106-116
    charting of, 114-115
    inventory, 107-109
    management of, 116-153
Body energy in hands-on
    therapy, 145-156
    See also Energy, body
Body/mind relationship,
    29-33
Body rhythms, 112-115
Bohm, D., 32
Boredom, 181
Bowen, M., 78, 80
Brain stem, 34
Brain, structure and func-
    tion, 34-39
    See also Left side of brain,
        Right side of brain
Brain wave activity, 130
Breath meditation, 139-141,
    217-219, 233
Breathing
    "circle," 140-141
    diaphragmatic, 140
    in reducing anxiety, 217-
        218

irregular, 49-50
meditation, 139-141
Brintzenhofe, S., 118, 121
Brown, G. W., 95
Bruxism, 58
Burnout
    management of, 20-21
    signs of, 16-20
    sources of, 18-20
Burns, D. D., 189, 190, 191,
    194

Caffeine, 121, 122
Calcium, 120
Cancer
    chemotherapy treatments,
        205
    effect of stress on, 59-60
    management of stress associ-
        ated with, 152-153,
        212-213
Cannon, W. B., 4, 41-48, 58,
    202, 207
Capra, F., 30
Cardiac output, 46, 48
Cardiovascular disorders
    as a result of stress, 48-50,
        56-58
    clinical example of stress
        management involving, 22-
        26
Cardiovascular system
    reaction of, to stress, 46,
        49, 56
    See also Hypertension,
        Myocardial infarction
Catatoxic steroids, 54, 57
Catecholamines, 46
Central nervous system, struc-
    ture and function, 33-39,
    44, 158
Cerebellum, 34
Change
    adapting to, 1-3

as a source of stress, 73-75,
    183
Characterological loneliness,
    236
Chemical pollutants, 68
Chemotherapy treatments, 205
Cholesterol plaques, 48, 49
Chronobiology, 112
Circadian cycle, 112-114,
    232, 235
Circulatory system, effect of
    stress on, 108
"Circle breathing," 140-141
Clarity, as characteristic of
    stressor, 8-9
Climate
    assessment of, 68
    management of, 88
Clothing, assessment of, 69,
    88
Code of honor, 265
Cognitive behavior
    changing of, 222
    therapy theory, 189-191
Cognitive disorders, Burns'
    list of, 190
Coherent sense of life, 9, 200
Color
    assessment of, 70-71
    management of, 90
Community environmental
    factors
    assessment of, 69, 72-73
    management of, 87-88,
    92-95
Compulsive behavior, 164, 230
Concentrative meditation,
    220-221
Concentrative relaxation,
    134-136
Conception model, 13-16
Conditioning factors, 56
Congestive heart failure, 48
Consciousness, identification
    of states of, 270
Conservation-withdrawal

behavior pattern, 53, 54,
    55-57, 59, 60
Contemplation, 272, 273-275
Control, 210
    and the defense response,
    54
    assessment of pattern of
    dealing with, 169-170
    conservation-withdrawal
    response, 53
    during anxiety, 162
    of environmental factor,
    66-67
    of response to stress, 186-
    187
    of stressors, 42
    self, 195-199
Controllability, as character-
    istic of stressor, 9
Coping, assessing styles of,
    165-168
Coping with stress, 60
    cognitive style of, 165-174
    learning methods of, 3
    personality style of, 174
Cortex, 34, 36, 38, 40, 54, 57
Corticoid activity, 51
Corticotropic hormone releas-
    ing factor (CRF), 54
Cortisone, 54, 55, 57
Counting meditation, 140,
    217-219, 233
Creativity, 187-188
Creighton, J., 152, 212
CRF. *See* Corticotropic hor-
    mone releasing factor
Cushing's syndrome, 50, 55,
    56, 58
Czeisler, C. A., 235

Death, focusing on idea of,
    275
Decision making, 241-242
Defeat, 53

Defense reaction. *See* Fight or
flight syndrome
Deleterious beliefs, 266
Denial
as a method of coping with
stress, 184
of addictive behavior,
237-238
of emotional responses, 201
Depression, 18, 50, 53, 56,
59, 60
as a stressor from social
understimulation, 181
assessment and management
of, 222-230
relationship between social
intimacy and, 95
Deprivation, 53
Descartes, 30
Desensitization method
to reduce anxiety, 221-222
to reduce anxiety associated
with sexual behavior, 240
to reduce fear, 204-206
to reduce loneliness, 236
Detachment, 185, 279
Diabetes, influence of stress
on, 59
Diaphragmatic breathing, 140
Diencephalon, 36
Diet and stress, 116-122
Disillusionment in burnout,
18
Distress, 51-52
defined, 5
physical reaction to, 107
Dizziness, 50
Dots, use of, in relaxation,
148, 149-150
Double-column technique to
enhance self-worth
beliefs, 191-193
to combat anxiety, 222
to combat depression, 228
to combat fear, 206
to help make decisions, 242

Dualism of mind and body, 30
Duration, as characteristic of
stressor, 8

Ecology, 86-87
Electromyograph (EMG), 131
Electromyograph biofeed-
back, 151
Ellis, A., 189
*Embrace Tiger, Return to
Mountain*, 142
EMG. *See* Electromyograph
Emmons, M. L., 197
Emotional manifestations of
stress, 160-164
Emotional responses, 4
and release of adrenaline,
46
self-regulation of, 201-241
Emotions
assessment of pattern of
dealing with, 170-172
suppression of, 59
Endocrine system, 40
Energy
as related to mind/body
unity, 30-32
fields in and around body,
145-147, 276
See also Polarity therapy
Energy, body in hands-on
therapy, 145-146
dynamics, 84
release of, under stress, 55
Energy field, 276
Energy foods, 119-120
Engham, Eunice, 145
Environment
ability to control, 66-67
as a source of stress, 65-66
defined, 65, 67
safety factors in, 69
signs of burnout in, 16-17
See also Personal environment, Physical environ-

ment, Social environment, Working environment, and World-wide environment

Environment, special, using imagery to create a, 219-220

Environmental action, 87

Enzymes, 55, 57

Eosinophils, effect of stress on, 57

Epilepsy, 131

Epinephrine, 40, 46

Esalen Institute, 142

Essence of our being, 251

Eustress, 51-52
    defined, 5

Exercise, 122-148, 234
    active, 122-128
    for flexibility, 125
    passive, 128-149
    rating of, 128
    sports chart, 129
    stretching, 126
    See also Relaxation

Exhaustion, 17
    phase of general adaptation syndrome, 51, 175

Expectations, unrealistic, 20

Failure, 53

Fainting spells, 50

Fairbank, D. T., 73

Fairness concept, in understanding anger, 209

Family Constellation, 99

Family system, 80-84
    management of stress related to, 96-99

Family therapy, 10

Fantasy, 187, 188

Fat deposits, 56

Fatigue, chronic, 17

Fatty acids, 49

Fear, 4, 46, 202-207
    See also Fight or flight

syndrome

Feedback, 177
    See also Biofeedback

Feedback loops, 30, 33, 36, 61, 157-158

Feeling Good, 190

Feelings. *See* Emotions

Feldenkrais method of relaxation, 141

Ferguson, Marilyn, 276-277

Fight or flight syndrome, 4, 39, 42-50, 58, 59, 123, 207, 216, 217

5-Day Allergy Relief System, 121

Flexibility, assessment of, as a sign of stress, 110-111
    exercises for, 125

Focusing the mind, 273

Food. *See* Nourishment

Foot Shiatsu, 145

Forgiveness, 214-215

Fox, M., 271

Frankl, V. E., 251

Free fatty acids, 49

Friedman, M., 48, 54, 176, 177

Frustration, 53, 163
    assessment of ability to cope with, 173-174

Galvanic skin response, 130

Gangrene, 49

Gastrointestinal tract
    disorders, as a result of stress, 57
    dysfunction of, 50, 51

General adaptation syndrome, 4, 42, 43
    consequences of the malfunction of, 52, 53-57, 58
    three states of, 50-52, 174-176

General excitation effect, 39

"Geographical cure," 185

Gestalt therapy, 10, 231, 253

Getting Well Again, 152
Gifford, S., 56
Glands, 40
Glucocorticoids, 40
Glucocorticoid hormones, 55
Glycogenesis, 55
Goal setting, 242-243
    assessment of, 172-173
Gonads, 40
Gordon, R., 146
Greater Power, defined, 253
Green, E. and A., 30
Grief
    inappropriate, 56
    unfinished as cause of
        distress, 160
Grieving process, related to
    unfinished relationships,
    228-229
Guided imagery, 137, 173-174
Guilt, 18, 162, 213-216
Gunderson, J. G., 56

Hair analysis, 121
Hands, warming of, as a
    relaxation response, 130
Hands-on methods of relax-
    ation, 142-146
Harper, R. A., 189
Hatha Yoga, 141
Hatred, as a source of stress,
    265
Headache
    from stress, 58
    treatment of, 145, 150-151
Healing
    ancient theories of, 10
    by touch, 142, 145-146
    modern theories of, 10-12
    through prayer, 275-276
Heart disease, relation to
    stress, 48-49
    See also Cardiovascular
        disorders

Heart muscle, thickening of,
    48
Heart rate, 46, 48, 49, 130
Helplessness, 18, 53
Henry, J. P., 46, 49, 252
Herman, S. J., 196
High threshold of arousal, 174
Hilts, P., 112
Holistic, defined, 10
Holistic approach to stress
    management, 56
    clinical situation illustrat-
        ing a, 22-26
Holistic health theory, 9-13
Holmes and Rahe Social
    Readjustment Rating
    Scale, 72-73, 74-75
Holograph theory of the
    universe, 32
Homeostasis, defined, 4
Hormones, 40, 43, 54-55,
    60-61
    ACTH, 54-56, 60
    CRF, 54
    STH, 54
    TTH, 54, 61
Hospital Stress Rating Scale,
    25
Hostility, 18
Hough, R. L., 73
Huang, A. C., 142
Hydrochloric acid secretion,
    57
Hyperadrenocorticism, 56
Hypertension, 45, 56, 131, 208
Hypnosis, 135-136
Hypothalamus, 36, 37, 40, 54,
    60, 61, 158, 252
Hypothalamic-pituitary-
    adrenal-cortical axis, 53

Imagery, 136-138, 188
    categories of, 137
    creating a special environ-
        ment through, 219-220

in activating the immune system, 152
in combating perfection-ism, 232
in combating sexual dys-function, 240-241
in coping with anxiety, 219-220
in coping with frustration, 173-174
in experiencing oneness of mind/body, 32-33
in management of addictive behavior, 239
in management of obesity, 150
in management of pain, 151-152
in practicing assertive behavior, 197-198
in ridding oneself of anger, 208-209
in ridding oneself of fear, 203-204
in ridding oneself of guilt, 214-215
in the grieving process, 229
Images, importance of, 195
Immune system dysfunction, as a result of stress, 50, 55, 57, 59, 60, 73-75, 152-153
Ineffectual beliefs, 265-266
Inflammation and the local adaptation syndrome, 53
effect of catatoxic steroids on, 55
effect of syntoxic steroids on, 55
Infradian cycle, 114
Inhibition, 50
Insomnia, 36, 232-235
effect of meditation on, 233
effect of stress on, 60-61
Inspiring beliefs, 265
Intensity

as characteristic of stressor, 7-8
of mental/emotional distress, 161-162
of reaction to stress, 52, 53
Internal experiential signs and symptoms of distress, 160-164
Interpersonal cognitive distortions, 199
Intimate relationships, as a way of managing stress, 95-96, 102
Intrapsychic route for eliciting defense reaction, 44-46
Introjected beliefs, 266
Irritation, 46
Isolation, 59

Jacobson, E., 132
James, W., 264-269
Johnson, V. E., 240
Jung, C. G., 251, 252

Kidney disease, effect of stress on, 48, 49
Kidneys, 40
Krieger, D., 146, 276
Krippner, S., 270, 276
Kuntzleman, C. T., 128

Lawlis, G. F., 137
Laying on of hands, healing by, 275-276
Lazarus, R. S., 148
Le Shan, L., 32, 59
Learning, suggestions for stress-free, 3
Left side of the brain, 38-39, 253, 270

Life change inventory, 72-73, 74-75
Life changes, adapting to, 1
Life style and stress management, 179-183
Life-threatening situations. *See* Fight or flight syndrome
Limbic system, 37-38, 44, 54, 158, 252
Lipid metabolism, effect of stress on, 49
"Live energy" foods, 119-120
Local adaptation syndrome, 53
Loneliness, 163, 181, 235-237
Loss, 6, 183, 222-223, 229-230
faulty grieving in connection with, 56
Loss of leadership, effect of, 95
Low alarm threshold, 174
Lowen, A., 141
L-tryptophan, 235
Luce, G. G., 114

MacLean, P. D., 33-34, 37
Magnesium, 120
Mandell, M., 121
Mantra, 220-221
Martyr role, 267
Maslow, A. H., 251, 278-279
Massage, 142-143, 229
Masters, W. H., 240
Meditation, 138-141, 188, 217-219, 220-221, 233, 272, 273-275
Medulla, 34, 40, 46
Meissner's Hospital Stress Rating Scale, 25
Mental/emotional problems
determining source of, 160-161
signs and symptoms of, 161-164, 216-217

Metabolism, 40, 49
Migraine headaches
as a result of stress, 58
treatment of, 150-151
Mind
defined, 12, 157-158
effect of stress on, 40-62
function of, in response to stressors, 158-160
managing stressors by managing the, 183-200
psychophysiology, review of, 33-40
signs and symptoms of distress in, 160
signs of burnout in, 17-18
Mind/body relationship, 29-33
Mindfulness, in meditation, 139
Mineralocorticoid hormones, 54
Mineralocorticoids, 40
Minerals, 120-121
Mirowsky, J., 73
Montague, A., 142
Moss, G. E., 102
Multiple sclerosis, 149, 161
Muscle tension, 130
as a sign of stress, 58, 110-111
charting of, 115-116
Myocardial infarction, 23, 48, 56
case study of client with, 23-24
Myocardial necrosis, 56-57
Mysticism, 30, 32

Nature, 87
assessment of time spent with, 71
Nausea, 49
Needs, simplification of, 86-87
Negative attitudes, 163

as a cause of depression, 223
as a sign of burnout, 17-18
assessment of pattern of coping with, 165-169
detrimental effect of, 190
Neocortex, 36, 38
Neocortical influence, 44
Neomammalian brain, 34, 38
Neuroendocrinology, 33, 46, 53
Neurotic guilt, 213, 214-216
Noise pollution, 68
management of, 89-90
Non-neurotic guilt, 213
Noradrenaline, 43, 46
Norepinephrine, 43, 46
Nourishment
as an environmental factor, 69
management of, 116-122
Nursing environment
management of stressors in, 20-21
stressors in, 18-20
Nurse Healers-Professional Associates Cooperative, 276
Nutrition and bodily distress, 116-122

Obesity, management of stress associated with, 149-150
Oceanic unity, 270
Ohashe, W., 143
One-pointedness, 273
Oriental massage, 143
Overcrowding, 89

Pacing, 244-245
Pain
as a result of stress, 58, 59
as a sign of burnout, 17

back, 131
management of, 150-152
neck, 131
Paleomammalian brain, 34, 36
Pancreas, 40
Parasympathetic nervous system, 39, 49-50
Parathyroids, 40
Peak experiences, 251, 278-279
Peck, S., 266
Perfectionism, 230-232
Personal environment, management of, 88
See also Environment
Personal mediating factors, 12, 65, 105, 157-158
Personality, 158
inventories, 160
styles of coping with stress, 174-179
Perspiration, assessment, for signs of distress, 108
Phobia, 131
Physical contact, healing by, 275-276
Physical environment
as a source of stress, 65
assessment of, 67-71
defined, 65-67
management of, 86-90
See also Environment
Physical fitness, test for, 124, 125
Physical space, 69-70
Physical symptoms of burnout, 17
Physics, quantum theory, as related to mind/body, 30-32
Pineal gland, 40
Pituitary-adrenal-cortical system, 43, 50
Pituitary gland, 40, 54
Polarity therapy, 146

Pollution
  assessment of, 68-69
  chemical, 68
  noise, 68
Pons, 34
Positive forces of the universe, 251
Posterior hypothalamus, 44
Posture, assessment of, for signs of distress, 110
Potassium, 120
Power, personal, 195-199
Power issues, assessment of pattern of dealing with, 169-170
Prayer, 271-272, 275
  defined, 271
  healing by, 275-276
Pribram, C., 32
Prioritizing
  in goal-setting, 243
  in time management, 244
Pritikin, N., 118
Probability, as characteristic of stressor, 8
Procrastination, 245
Professional assistance, assessing need for, 26
Progressive relaxation, 132-134
Proinflammatory hormones, 54
Psychopathology, relation of stress to, 60
Psychophysiologic functions, monitoring of, 130-131
Psychophysiology
  defined, 29-32
  review of, 33-40
Psychosis, 60, 164
Psychosomatic medicine, 30
Pulse rate, 111

Quantum physics theory, 30
Quiet time, 89

Rage, 4
Rahe, R. H. *See* Holmes and Rahe Social Readjustment Rating Scale
Rama, S., 140
RAS. *See* Reticular activating system
Rating the Exercises, 128
Rational-emotive therapy, 189-199
Reactive hypoglycemia, 122
Realms of Healing, 276
Reciprocity, 80, 97-98
Reconstructed imagery, 137
Reflexology, 142, 145
Relationships, importance of, 201-202
Relaxation
  active, to manage bodily distress, 122-130
  concentrative, 220-221
  Feldenkrais method, 141
  passive, to manage bodily distress, 129-130, 137-138
  progressive, 132-134
  See also Acupressure, Autogenics, Bioenergetics, Exercise, Imagery, Massage, Meditation
Relaxation response, 188
  general, 122
Relaxation Response, The, 221
Relaxation Tapes, 21-22, 136, 180, 229, 233
Religions, Values and Peak Experiences, 278-279
Religious, defined, 252
Repression of emotional responses, 201
Reptilian brain, 34
Resentments, 59, 209
  exercise to rid oneself of, 212-213
  methods of dealing with, 211-213

Resistance, lowering of, 50
Resistance phase of general
    adaptation syndrome, 50-
    51, 175
Respiration, 111
Responsibility, 210, 236-237
Reticular activating system
    (RAS), 34-36, 54, 61, 128,
    158, 188
Revenge as a source of stress,
    265
Rewards to control addictive
    behavior, 238
Reynaud's disease, 131
Rheumatoid arthritis,
    influence of stress on,
    58-59
Rhythms, body, 112-116
Right side of the brain, 38-39,
    137, 252, 253
Rights of human beings,
    196-197
Road Less Traveled, The, 266
Role-playing, 80-82, 98-100,
    267
Rosenman, R. H., 48, 54,
    176-177
Roseto community, 66, 92-93
Ross, C. E., 73
Rules, as a factor in determin-
    ing role-playing, 80

Safe place, using imagery to
    create a, 219-220
Safety
    assessment of, 69
    management of, 88-89
Salt, 121-122
Salt retention, 56
Satir, V., 80-82
Schultz, J., 134
Science, as compared to
    spiritual philosophies, 253
Scully, R., 19-20

Self-actualization, 251
Self-critical thoughts, identifi-
    cation of, 191-194
Self-esteem, lowered, 20, 163
Self-help groups, 94
Self-regulation of beliefs,
    186-200
Self-responsibility, in stress
    management, 12
Self-transformation, 188
Selye, H., 4-5, 9-10, 42-43,
    50-51, 58-59, 265
Sense of unity, 251, 253
Sexual dysfunction, 164,
    239-241
    using imagery in combating,
    240-241
Sexual energy during burn-
    out, 17
Shamans, 10
Shapiro, D. H., 138
Shiatsu, 143-145
"Shoulds," thoughts, as a
    source of anger, 209-210
Sierra Club, 87
Silent Killer, 48
Simonton, O. C. and S., 152,
    212
Situational loneliness, 236
Skin, assessment of, for signs
    of distress, 107-108
Skin surface temperature, 130
Sleep disorders, 17-18
    See also Insomnia
Social environment
    as a source of stress, 13,
    65-66, 72-86
    assessment of, 72-86
    defined, 65-67
    management of, 90-103
    See also Environment
Social intimacy, 95-96
Social isolation, 181
Social life style and stress
    management, 179-183
Social Readjustment Rating

Scale (SRRS), 72-73,
74-75
Social systems, types of, 78-79
Social systems theory, 10, 72,
73, 76-85, 187
applied to social environment, 82
concept of reciprocity in,
80
roles in, 80
types of, 80
Solar Lobby, 87
Solitude, 181
Somatotrophic hormone
(STH), 54
Space, physical
assessment of, 69-70
in promoting sleep, 234
management of, 89
Spinal column pain, 58
Spirit
defined, 12-13, 251
signs of burnout of, 18
Spiritual, defined, 252
Spiritual beliefs
as a way to manage stress,
264-279
as compared to scientific
beliefs, 253
assessment of, 254, 255-264
categories of influence of,
265-266
Spiritual crisis, 265
Spiritual development,
pattern of, 250
Spiritual experience,
source of, 251-254
Spleen, 40
Spontaneous imagery, 137
Sports, chart, 129
SRRS. *See* Social Readjustment Rating Scale
States of consciousness,
identification of, 270
Steroids. *See* Syntoxic,
Cortisone, Catatoxic

Stevens, P. M., 46, 49, 252
Stomach, effect of stress on,
57
Stomach ulcers, 50
Storlie, F. J., 16, 21
Stress
addiction to, 26
defined, 3-5, 50
flexibility, as a sign of,
110-111
importance of managing,
1-2
Stress management
clinical approach to, 22-26
educational approach to,
21-22
holistic approach to, 21-26
Stress rating scale, 25
Stress response, 6
alarm, as reaction to, 50
as a normal mechanism,
40-41
as defined by Selye, 5
defined, 5
See also Professional
burnout
Stress Without Distress, 265
Stressors
ambiguous, 42
characteristics of, 6-9
clear, 42
constant, 42
defined, 5-6
effects of, 42
internal, 19-20
normal, 40-41
origins, 13
precipitating burnout,
18-19
relation of disease to, 58-62
Stretching exercises, 126-127
Stroke, 56
Substance dependency, 164
assessment of, 177-179
Sugar, 121, 122
Suppression of emotional

responses, 201
Sympathetic-adrenal-medullary
  system, 53, 206
  effect of stress on, 43, 49,
  53
Sympathetic nervous system,
  39, 42, 44, 46, 48, 49
Syntoxic steroids, 54, 55, 57
Systems Theory. *See* Social
  Systems Theory

Tai Chi Chuan, 142
Tapes
  relaxation, 21-22, 136, 180,
  229, 233, 239
  "Suggestions for General
    Relaxation," 21-22,
    180, 233
  hypnotic, 234
  "Suggestions for Restful
    Sleep," 234
Temperature, assessment of,
  for signs of distress, 108
Temporomandibular joint
  syndrome, 58, 131
Tension, body
  as a sign of anger, 208
  as a sign of stress, 58, 110
  charting of, 114-115
  headaches, 58, 131
  release of. *See* Relaxation
Thalamus, 36-37
Therapeutic Touch, The, 276
Thie, John, 145
Threatening situation. *See*
  Fight or flight syndrome
Three Boxes of Life, The, 256
Thresholds of arousal, 174-176
Thymico-lymphatic atrophy,
  51
Thymus, 40
Thyroid gland, 40
Thyrotropic hormone (TTH),
  54, 61
Thyroxin, 40, 61

Time Management, 243-245
  assessment of, 182-183
Tissue dysfunction, 49
Titering concept, 228-229
Toman, W., 99
Touch, healing by, 142-146,
  275-276
Touch for health, 142, 145
Transcendent experiences,
  277-279
Transpersonal psychology,
  251-252
Triangle relationship, 97
Triune brain, 34
Tsubo, 143
TTH. *See* Thyrotropic
  hormone
Tumor regression, 60
Two-column method
  to combat anxiety, 222
  to combat depression, 228
  to combat fear, 206
  to enhance self-worth
    beliefs, 191-193
  to help make decisions, 242
*Type A Behavior and Your
  Heart,* 176
Type A personality, 53-54,
  176, 177, 243
Type B personality, 54,
  176-177

Ulcers, 50, 57
Unconscious, as source of
  spiritual experience, 251
Universal Declaration of
  Human Rights, 197

Vagotonia, 49-50
Vaillant, G. E., 250
Values, 256-264
*Varieties of Religious Expe-
  rience, The,* 264, 269-270
Vasculature of kidneys, 49

Vasoconstriction of blood
     vessels, 48
Vasopressin, 40
Villoldo, A., 276
Visualization, 32-33, 136-138,
     231, 239, 240. *See also*
     Imagery
Vitamins, 118, 119-120
Vitamin B, 120, 122

Walster, E. and G. W., 2
Water, in diet, importance of
     adequate, 120
Water retention, 56
Way to Vibrant Health, The,
     141
Weitzman, E. D., 235
Wellness, concept of, 12
"What if" exercise, 204
Wholeness
     concept of, 10, 30
     of human beings, 251-252,
        279
Withdrawal, 50
     as a method of coping with
        stress, 184-185
Wolpe, J., 204
Working environment
     management of stressors
        in, 20-21
     stressors in, 18-20
World-wide environment
     assessment of, 72-73
     management of, 91-92

Yoga, 141
Your Healing Hands, 146
Your Health Under Seige, 121
Your Perfect Right, 197

Zone therapy, 145

TAPES FROM LYNN BRALLIER

If you wish to order the cassette tapes mentioned in this book, complete the order form below.

ORDER FORM

Please send me the following cassette tape(s):

_____ Copy(ies) of "Suggestions for General Relaxation"

_____ Copy(ies) of "Suggestions for Restful Sleep"

Price is $9.95 each plus $1.00 postage and handling.

I have enclosed my check or money order for _____

Make Payable to: Lynn W. Brallier, M.S.N.

Send to:
   Stress Management Center of Metropolian Washington
   621 Maryland Avenue, N.E.
   Washington, D.C. 20002

Name (print) _____

Address _____

City/State_____ Zip _____

Allow two weeks for delivery.